play guitar w[illegible]

the 60[illegible]s

GW00836728

Wise Publications
London/New York/Paris/Sydney/Copenhagen/Madrid

Music Sales Limited
*8-9 Frith Street,
London W1V 5TZ, England.*
Music Sales Pty Limited
*120 Rothschild Avenue,
Rosebery, NSW 2018, Australia.*

Order No. AM957748
ISBN 0-7119-7876-X

*Music compiled and arranged by Arthur Dick
Music processed by Andrew Shiels
Cover photographs courtesy of
London Features International*

*Printed in the United Kingdom by
Caligraving Limited, Thetford, Norfolk.*

*CD programmed by John Moores
Recorded by Kester Sims
Guitar preparation by Charlie Chandler at Chandler Guitars
All guitars by Arthur Dick
Harmonica on 'Not Fade Away' by Stuart Constable
Drums on 'I Can See For Miles' by Paul Kemp
Bass on 'I Can See For Miles' by Paul Townsend
With special thanks to Andy Milner at Marshall for supply of amplification*

all along the watchtower jimi hendrix
12
all day and all of the night the kinks
6
back in the ussr the beatles
26
born to be wild steppenwolf
21
help! the beatles
36
i can see for miles the who
40
not fade away the rolling stones
47
sunshine of your love cream
52
guitar tablature explained
4
translations
61

guitar tablature explained

Guitar music can be notated three different ways: on a musical stave, in tablature, and in rhythm slashes

RHYTHM SLASHES are written above the stave. Strum chords in the rhythm indicated. Round noteheads indicate single notes.

THE MUSICAL STAVE shows pitches and rhythms and is divided by lines into bars. Pitches are named after the first seven letters of the alphabet.

TABLATURE graphically represents the guitar fingerboard. Each horizontal line represents a string, and each number represents a fret.

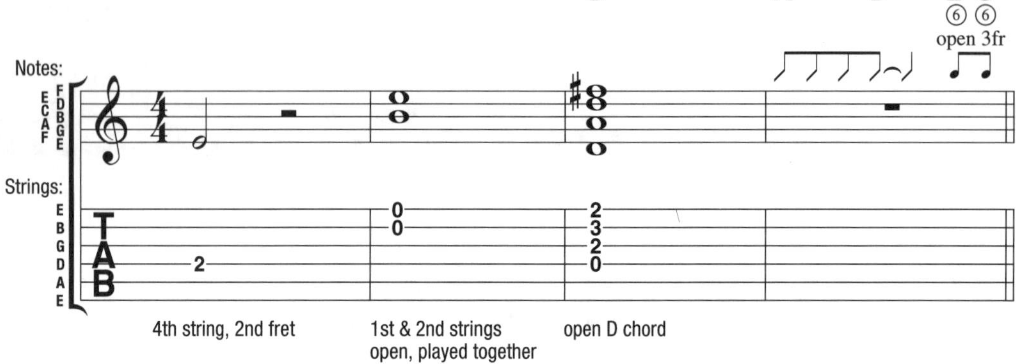

definitions for special guitar notation

SEMI-TONE BEND: Strike the note and bend up a semi-tone (1/2 step).

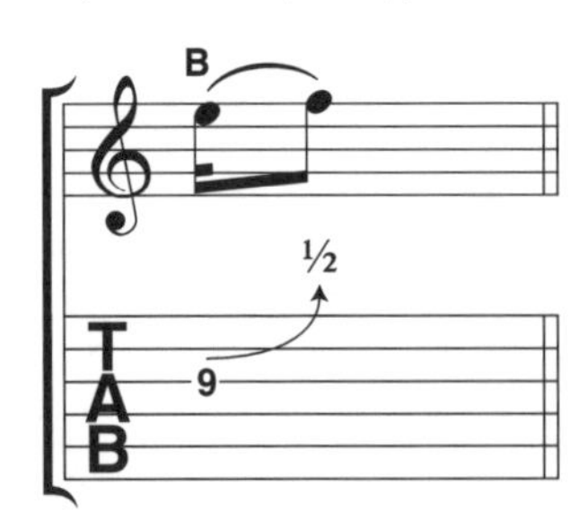

WHOLE-TONE BEND: Strike the note and bend up a whole-tone (whole step).

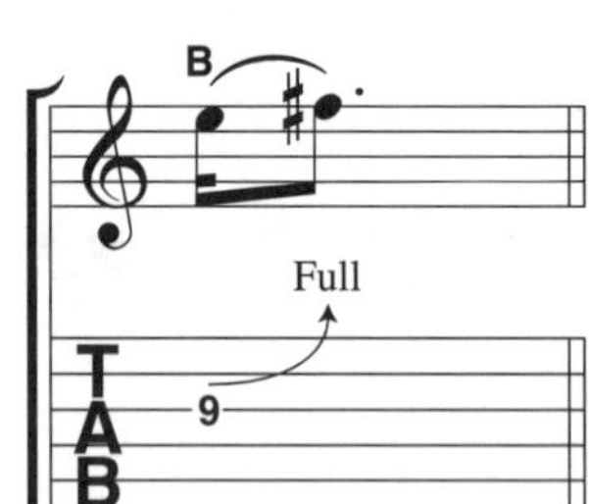

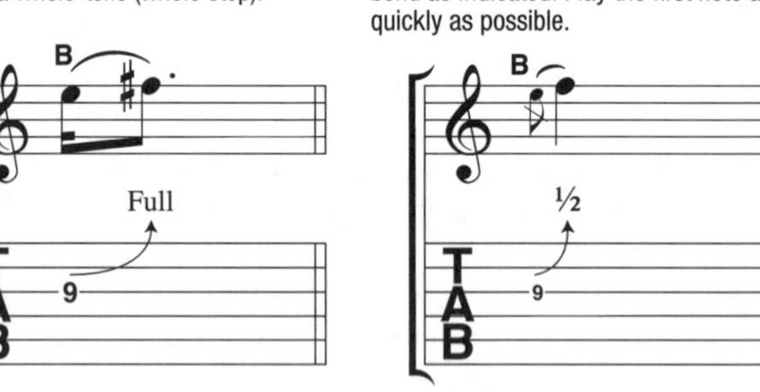

GRACE NOTE BEND: Strike the note and bend as indicated. Play the first note as quickly as possible.

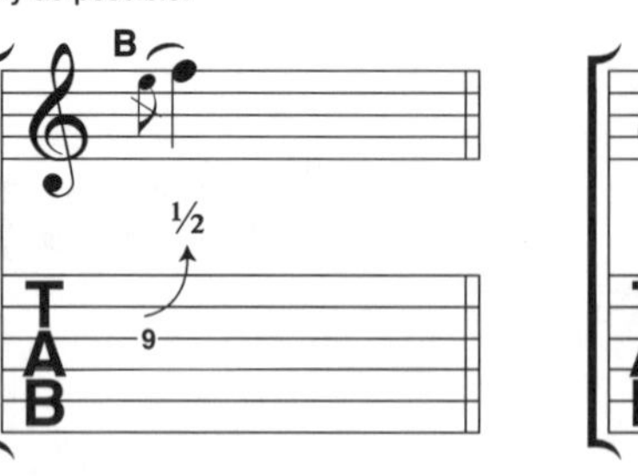

QUARTER-TONE BEND: Strike the note and bend up a 1/4 step.

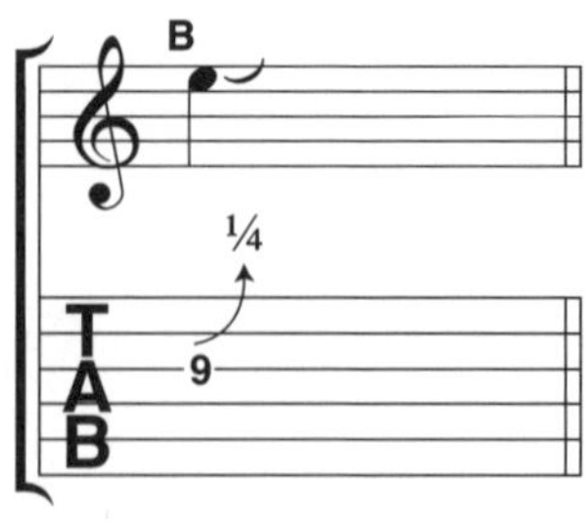

BEND & RELEASE: Strike the note and bend up as indicated, then release back to the original note.

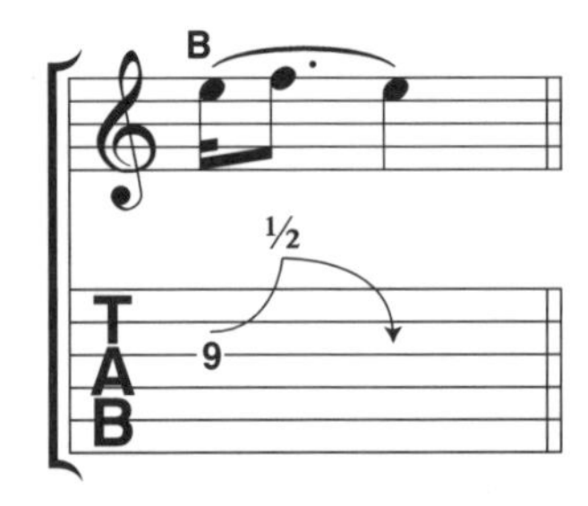

COMPOUND BEND & RELEASE: Strike the note and bend up and down in the rhythm indicated.

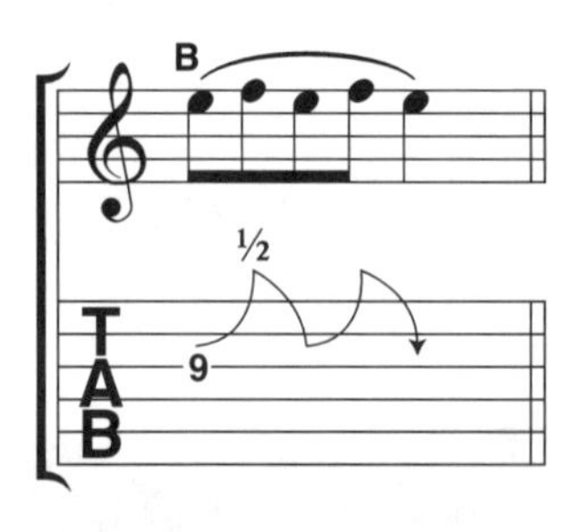

PRE-BEND: Bend the note as indicated, then strike it.

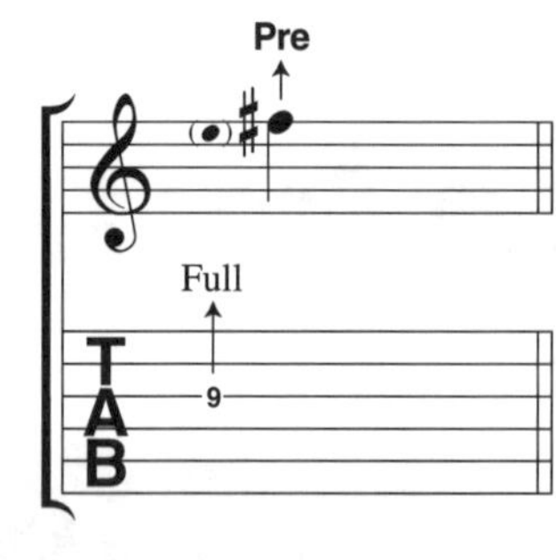

PRE-BEND & RELEASE: Bend the note as indicated. Strike it and release the note back to the original pitch.

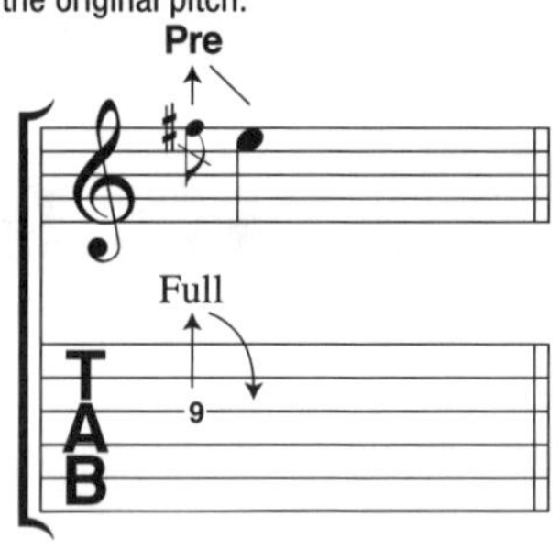

UNISON BEND: Strike the two notes simultaneously and bend the lower note up to the pitch of the higher.

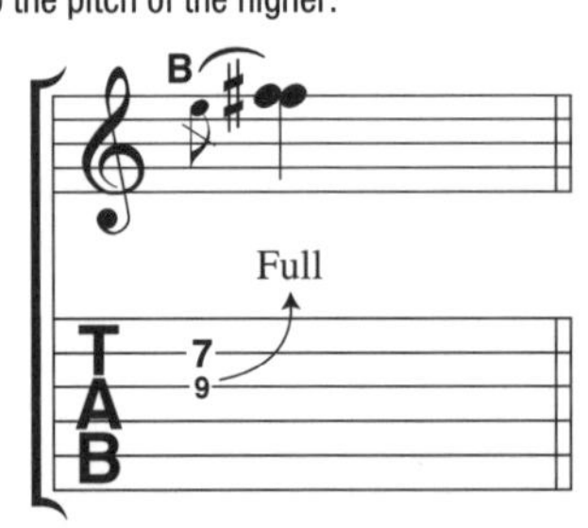

BEND & RESTRIKE: Strike the note and bend as indicated then restrike the string where the symbol occurs.

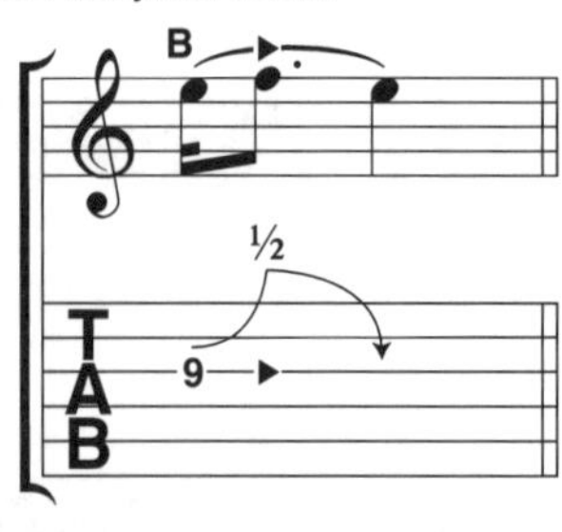

BEND, HOLD AND RELEASE: Same as bend and release but hold the bend for the duration of the tie.

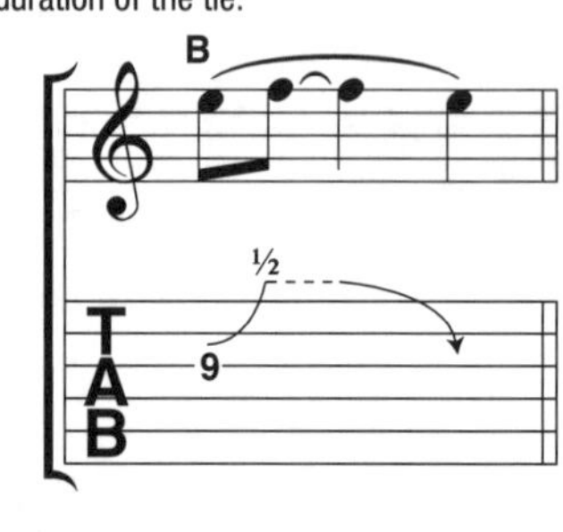

BEND AND TAP: Bend the note as indicated and tap the higher fret while still holding the bend.

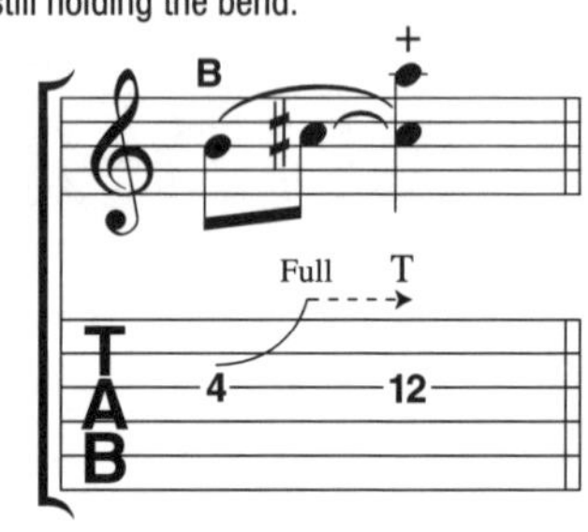

VIBRATO: The string is vibrated by rapidly bending and releasing the note with the fretting hand.

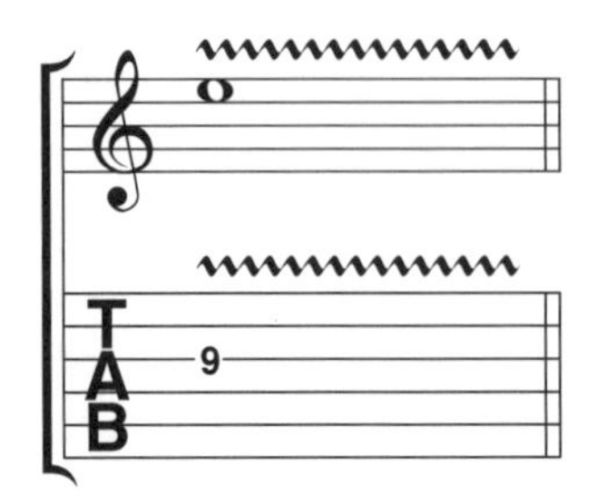

HAMMER-ON: Strike the first (lower) note with one finger, then sound the higher note (on the same string) with another finger by fretting it without picking.

PULL-OFF: Place both fingers on the notes to be sounded, Strike the first note and without picking, pull the finger off to sound the second (lower) note.

LEGATO SLIDE (GLISS): Strike the first note and then slide the same fret-hand finger up or down to the second note. The second note is not struck.

NOTE: The speed of any bend is indicated by the music notation and tempo.

SHIFT SLIDE (GLISS & RESTRIKE): Same as legato slide, except the second note is struck.

TRILL: Very rapidly alternate between the notes indicated by continuously hammering on and pulling off.

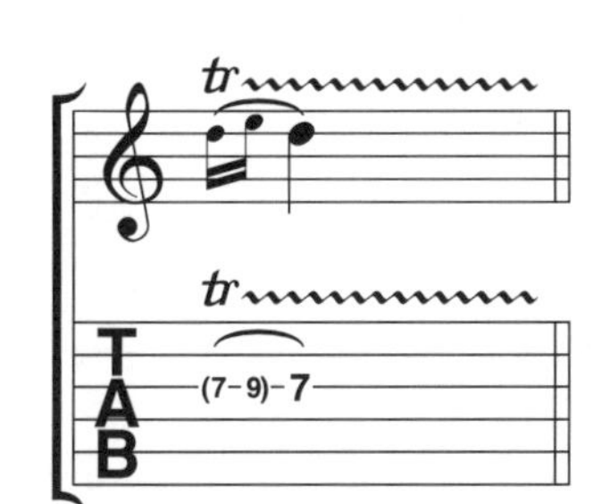

TAPPING: Hammer ("tap") the fret indicated with the pick-hand index or middle finger and pull off to the note fretted by the fret hand.

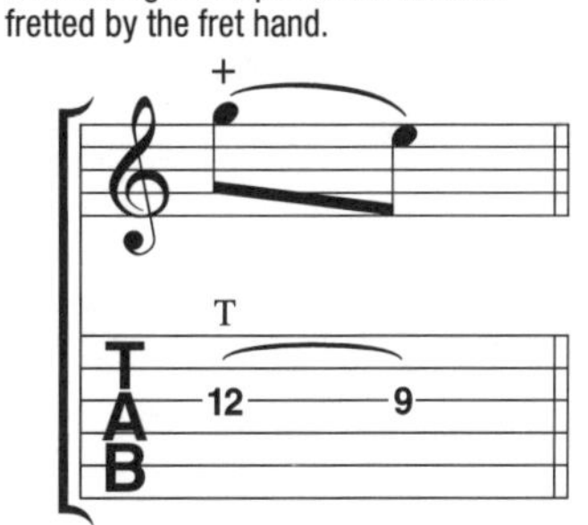

PICK SCRAPE: The edge of the pick is rubbed down (or up) the string, producing a scratchy sound.

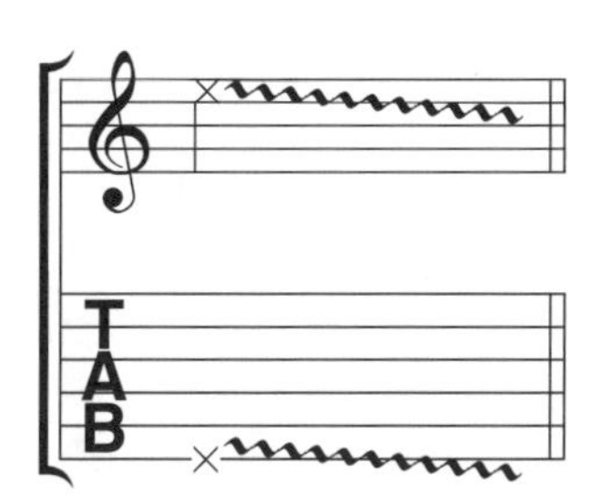

MUFFLED STRINGS: A percussive sound is produced by laying the fret hand across the string(s) without depressing, and striking them with the pick hand.

NATURAL HARMONIC: Strike the note while the fret-hand lightly touches the string directly over the fret indicated.

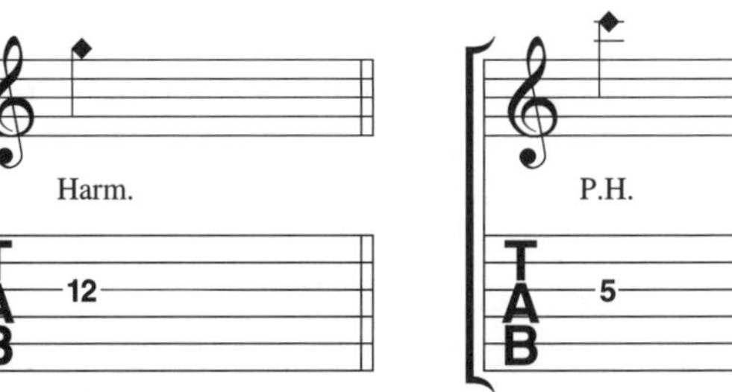

PINCH HARMONIC: The note is fretted normally and a harmonic is produced by adding the edge of the thumb or the tip of the index finger of the pick hand to the normal pick attack.

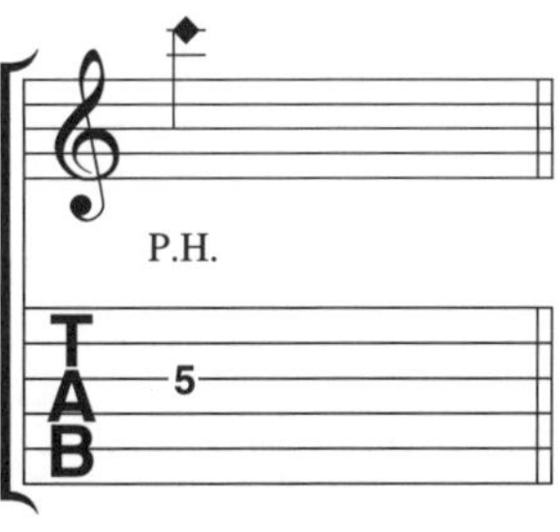

HARP HARMONIC: The note is fretted normally and a harmonic is produced by gently resting the pick hand's index finger directly above the indicated fret (in parentheses) while the pick hand's thumb or pick assists by plucking the appropriate string.

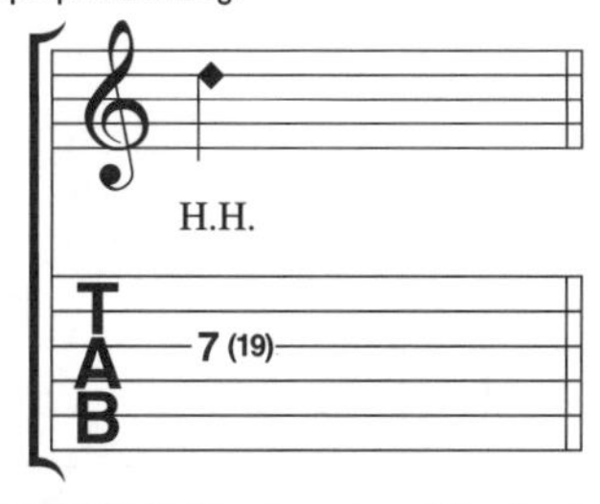

PALM MUTING: The note is partially muted by the pick hand lightly touching the string(s) just before the bridge.

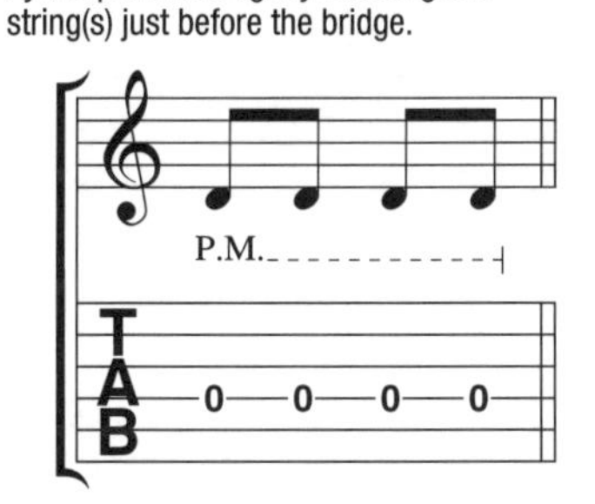

RAKE: Drag the pick across the strings indicated with a single motion.

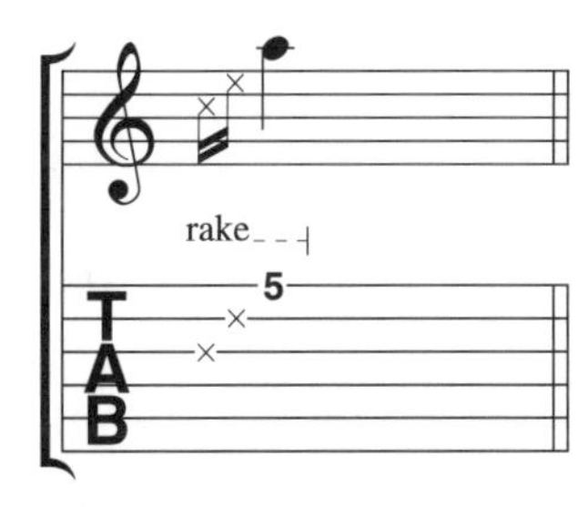

TREMOLO PICKING: The note is picked as rapidly and continuously as possible.

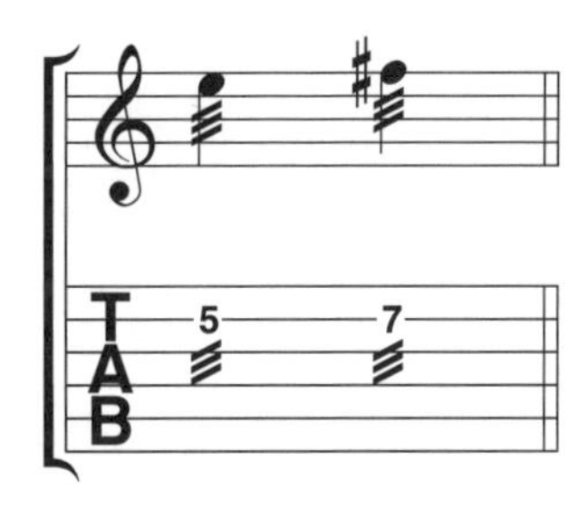

ARPEGGIATE: Play the notes of the chord indicated by quickly rolling them from bottom to top.

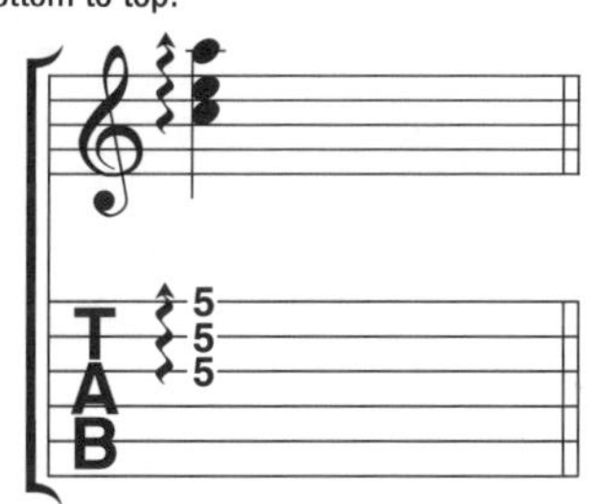

SWEEP PICKING: Rhythmic downstroke and/or upstroke motion across the strings.

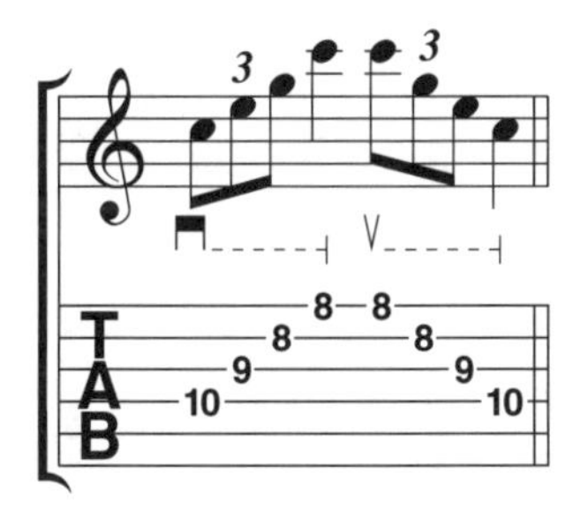

VIBRATO DIVE BAR AND RETURN: The pitch of the note or chord is dropped a specific number of steps (in rhythm) then returned to the original pitch.

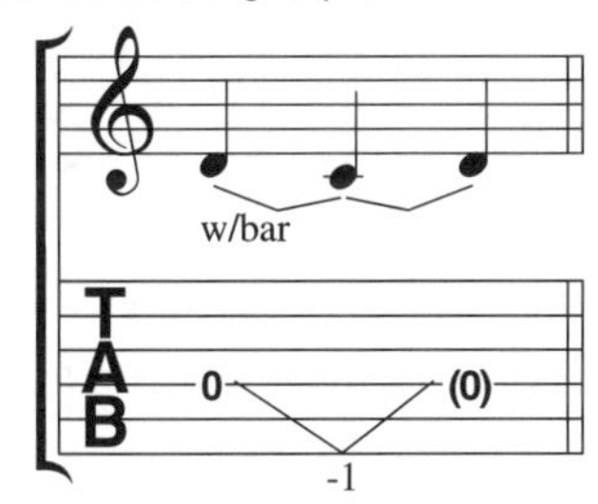

VIBRATO BAR SCOOP: Depress the bar just before striking the note, then quickly release the bar.

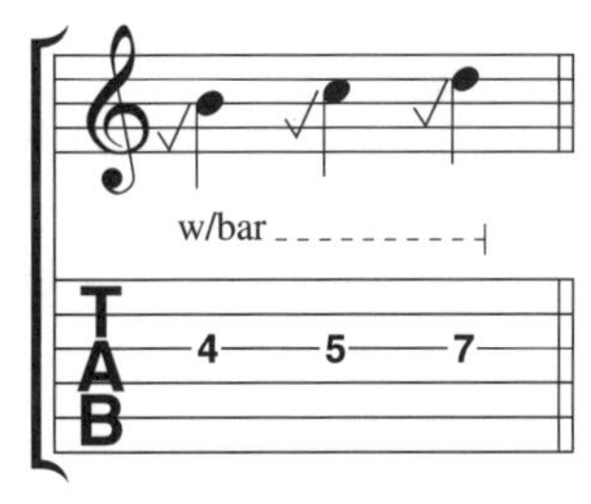

VIBRATO BAR DIP: Strike the note and then immediately drop a specific number of steps, then release back to the original pitch.

additional musical definitions

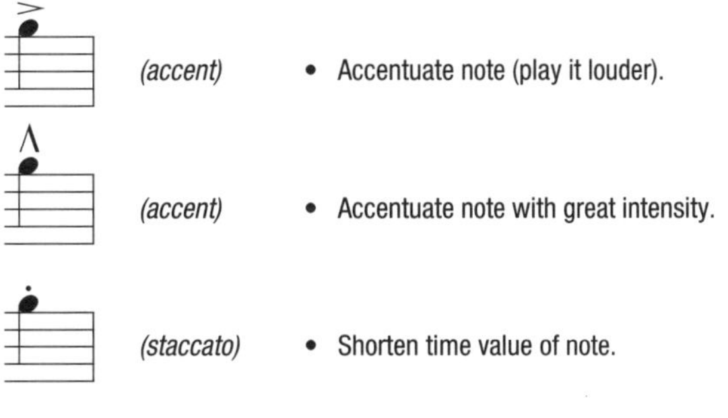

- (accent) • Accentuate note (play it louder).
- (accent) • Accentuate note with great intensity.
- (staccato) • Shorten time value of note.
- • Downstroke
- • Upstroke

D.%. al Coda • Go back to the sign (%), then play until the bar marked ***To Coda*** ⊕ then skip to the section marked ⊕ ***Coda***.

D.C. al Fine • Go back to the beginning of the song and play until the bar marked ***Fine*** (end).

tacet • Instrument is silent (drops out).

• Repeat bars between signs.

1. 2. • When a repeated section has different endings, play the first ending only the first time and the second ending only the second time.

NOTE: Tablature numbers in parentheses mean:
1. The note is sustained, but a new articulation (such as hammer on or slide) begins.
2. A note may be fretted but not necessarily played.

all day and all of the night

Words & Music by Ray Davies

G5 F5 Bb5 G5 F5 G5 F5
Girl I want to be with_ you all of the_ time.
Bb5 G5 Bb5 F
The on - ly time I feel al - right_ is by your_
A G C A
Chorus
D C
_ side._
Girl I want to
F D C F D C
be with_ you all of the_ time, all day and all of the night,_

D C F D C D C
all day and all of the night, all day and
F D
all of the night.
Verse
G5 F5 B♭5 G5 F5
2. I believe that you and me last forev-
G5 F5 B♭5 G5 F5 G5 F5
-er. Oh yeah, all day and
B♭5 G5 F5 G5 F5 B♭5 G5
night I'm yours leave me ne - ver. The
TAB

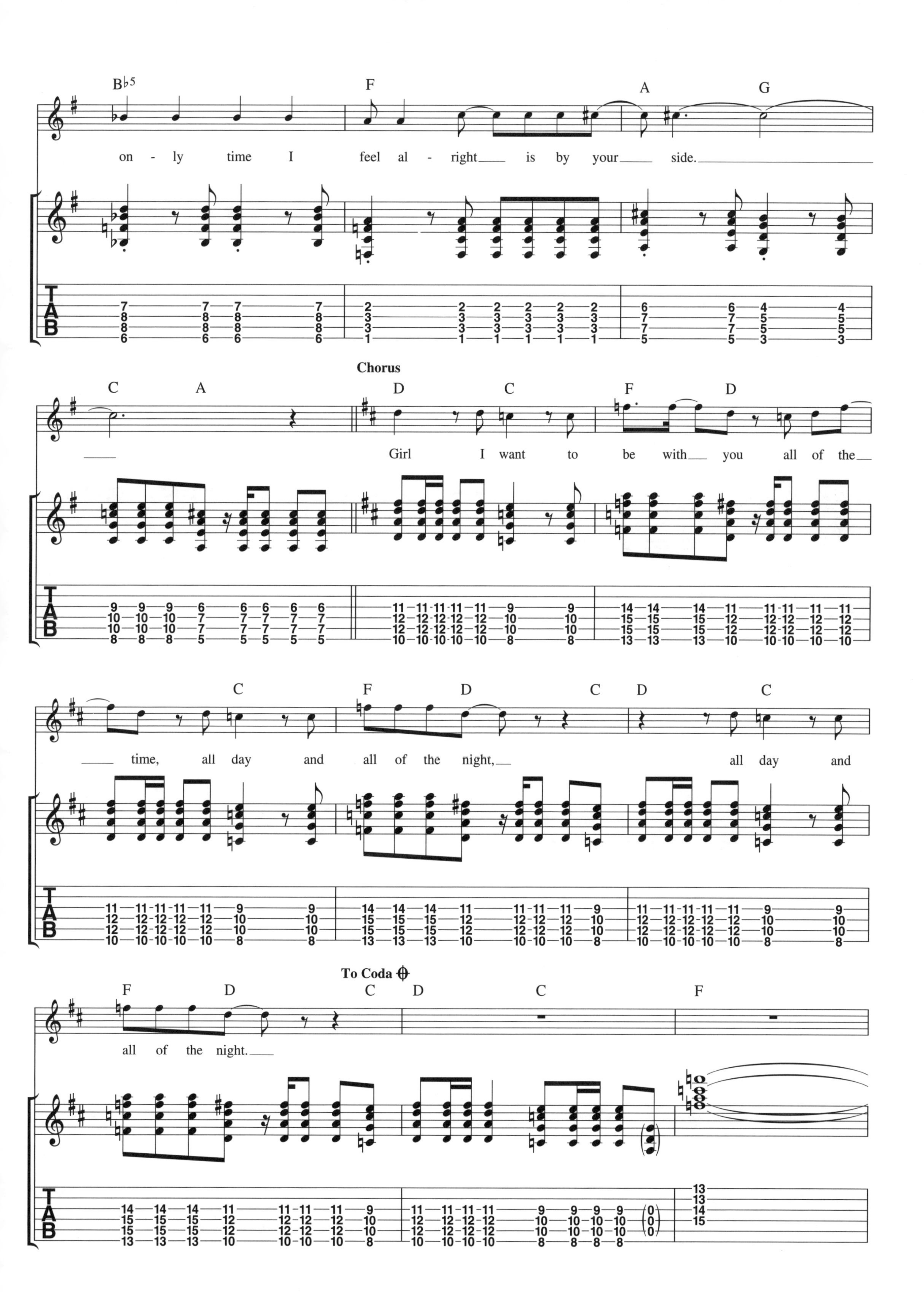
B♭5 F A G
only time I feel al - right is by your side.
C A
Chorus
D C F D
Girl I want to be with you all of the
C F D C D C
time, all day and all of the night, all day and
To Coda
F D C D C F
all of the night.
TAB

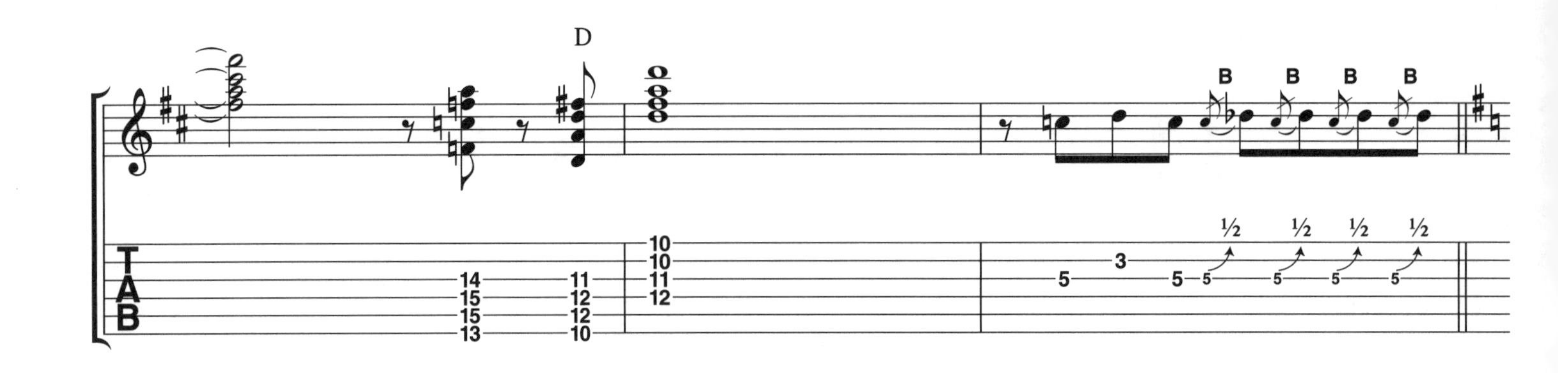
D
B B B B
½ ½ ½ ½

Solo

G5
F5
B♭5
G5
F5
½
Full

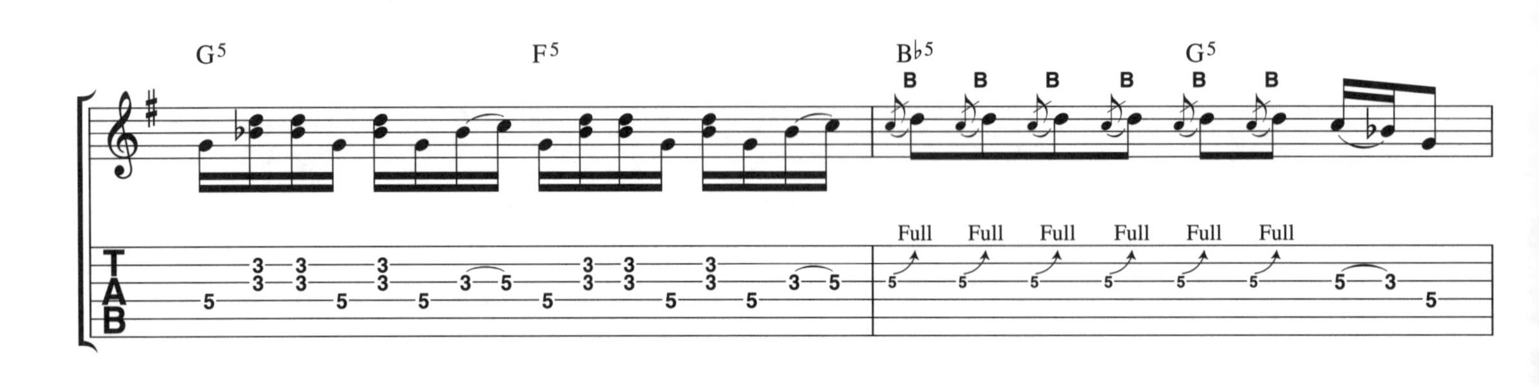
G5
F5
B♭5
G5
B B B B B B
Full Full Full Full Full Full

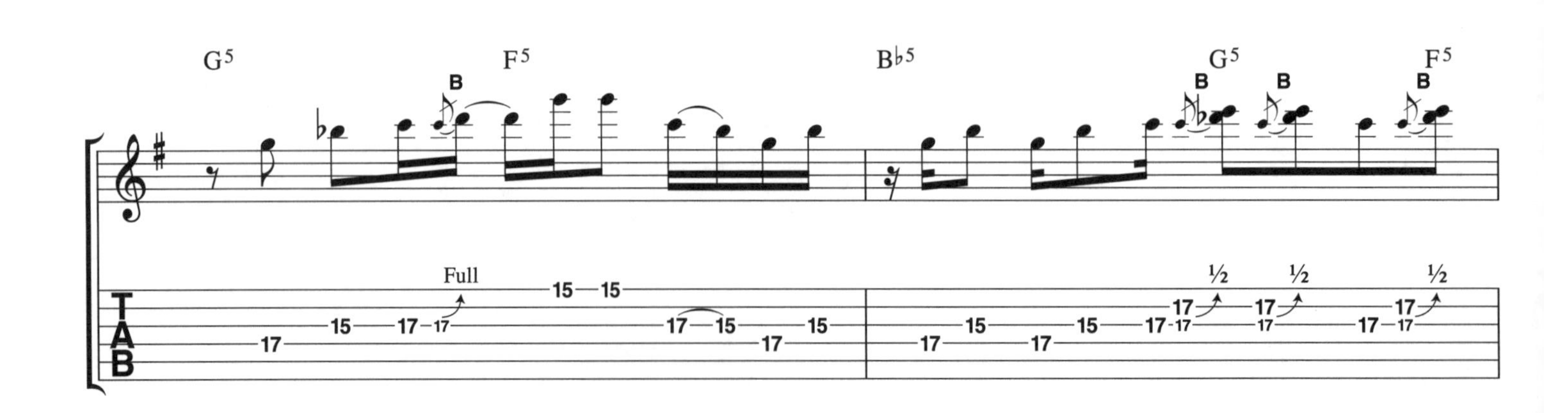
G5
F5
B
Full
B♭5
G5
F5
B B B
½ ½ ½

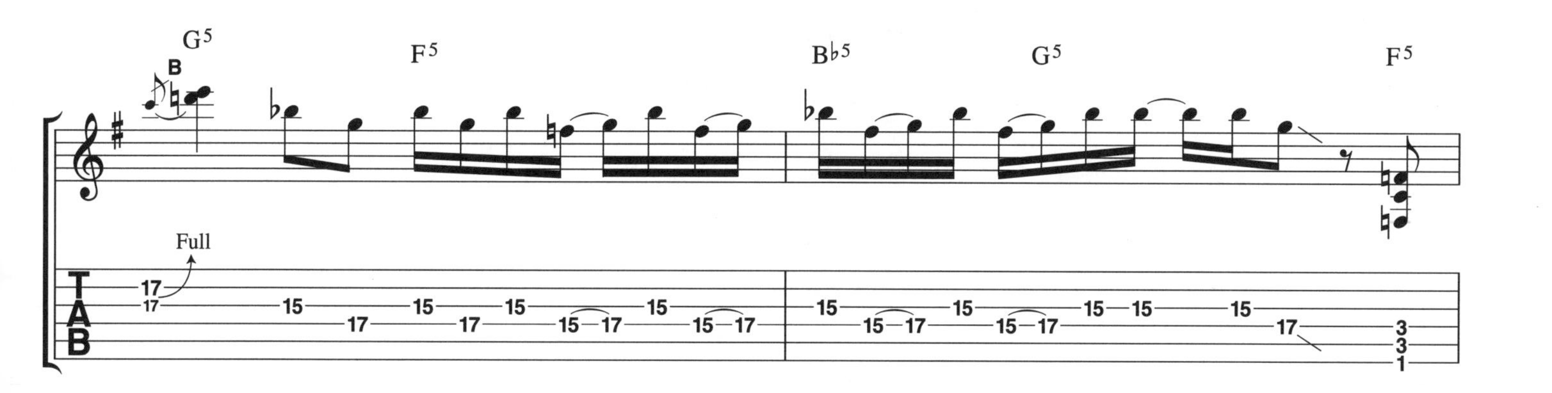
G5
B
F5
B♭5
G5
F5
Full
T
A
B

D.S. al Coda
G5
F5
B♭5
G5
F5
Coda
D
C
F
D
all day and all of the night,
D
C
F
D

all along the watchtower

Words & Music by Bob Dylan

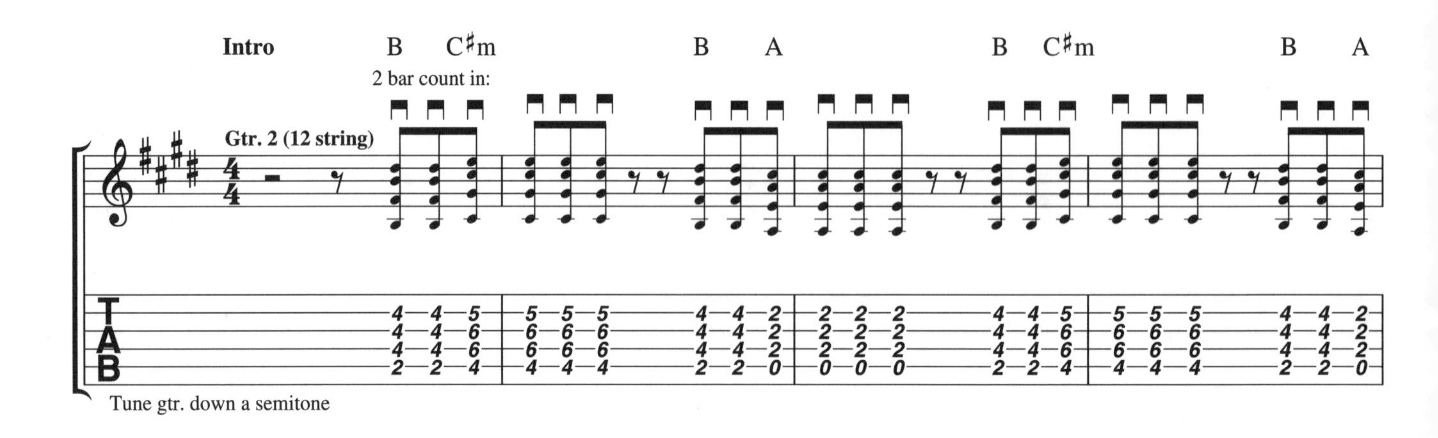

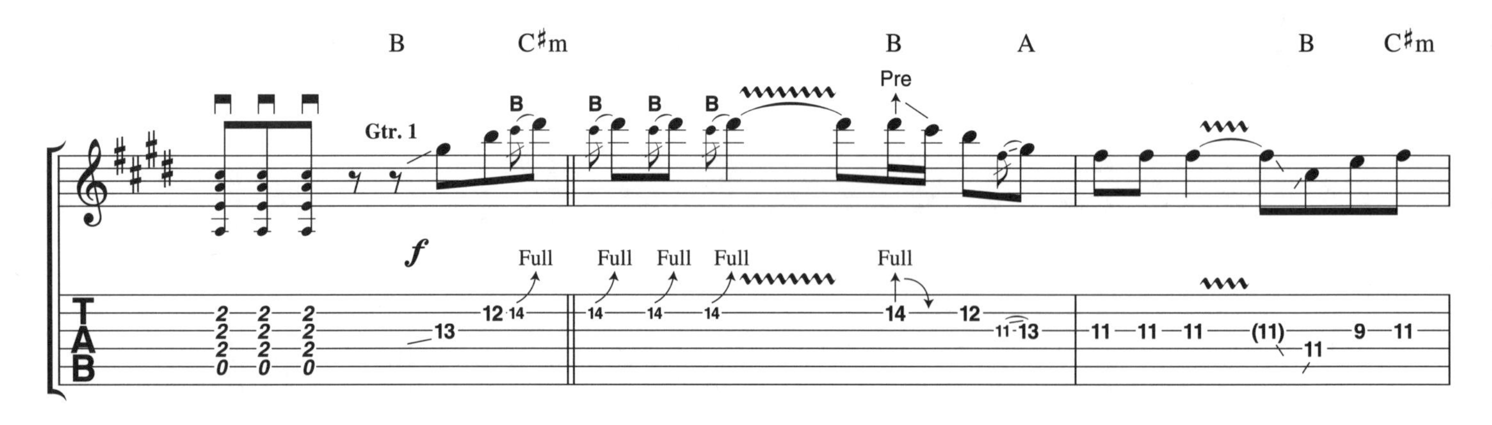

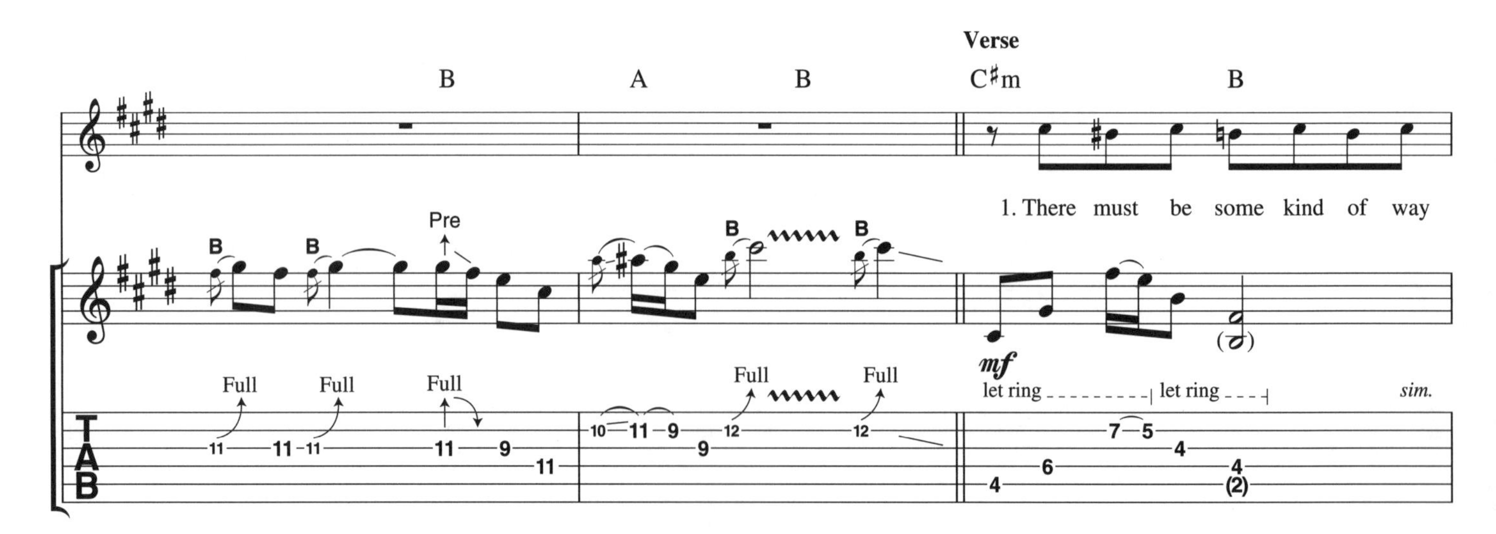

A B C♯m B A B
outta here said the joker to the thief.
C♯m B A B C♯m B
There's too much confusion, I can't get no relief.
A B C♯m B A B
Business men, they ah ah, drink my wine,
C♯m B A B C♯m B
plow men dig my earth. None will level on
TAB

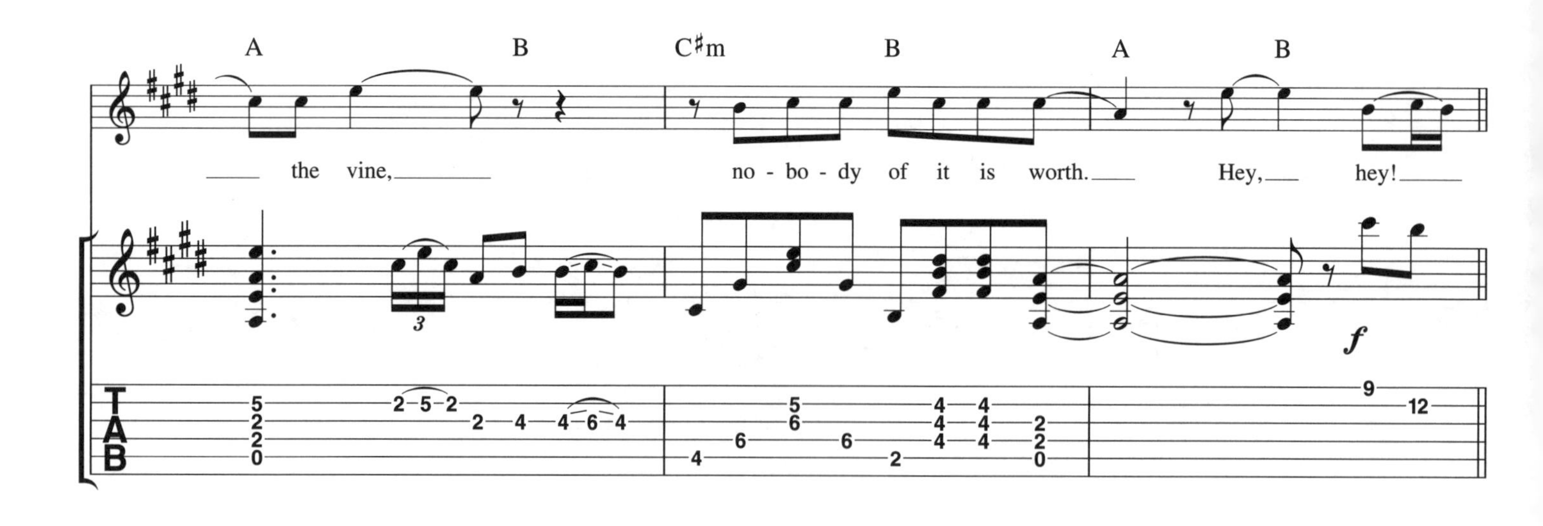
A B C♯m B A B
the vine, no - bo - dy of it is worth. Hey, hey!
TAB

Solo

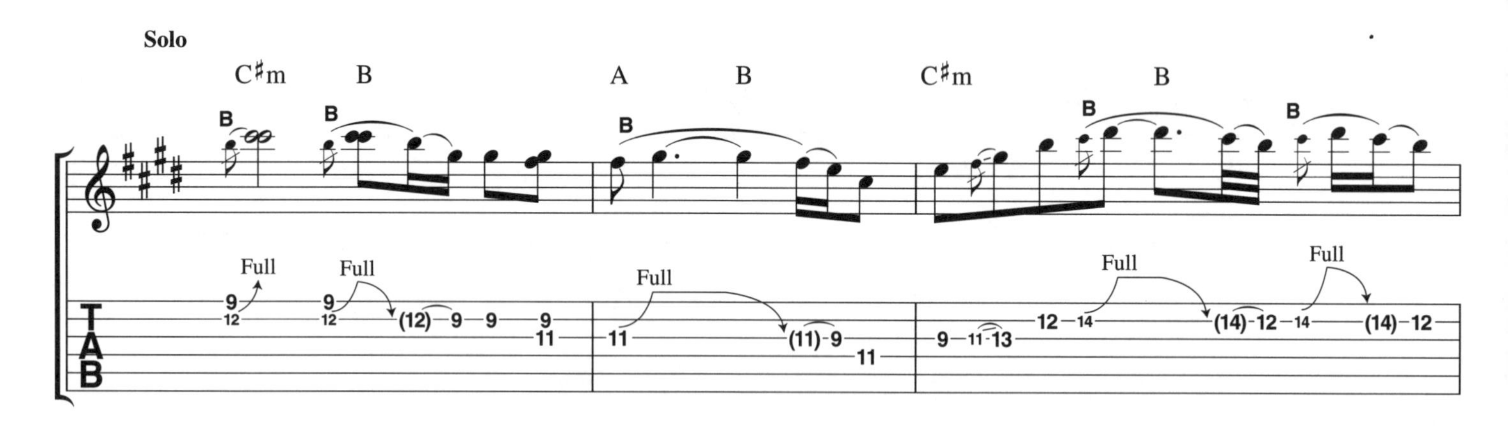
C♯m B A B C♯m B
Full
TAB

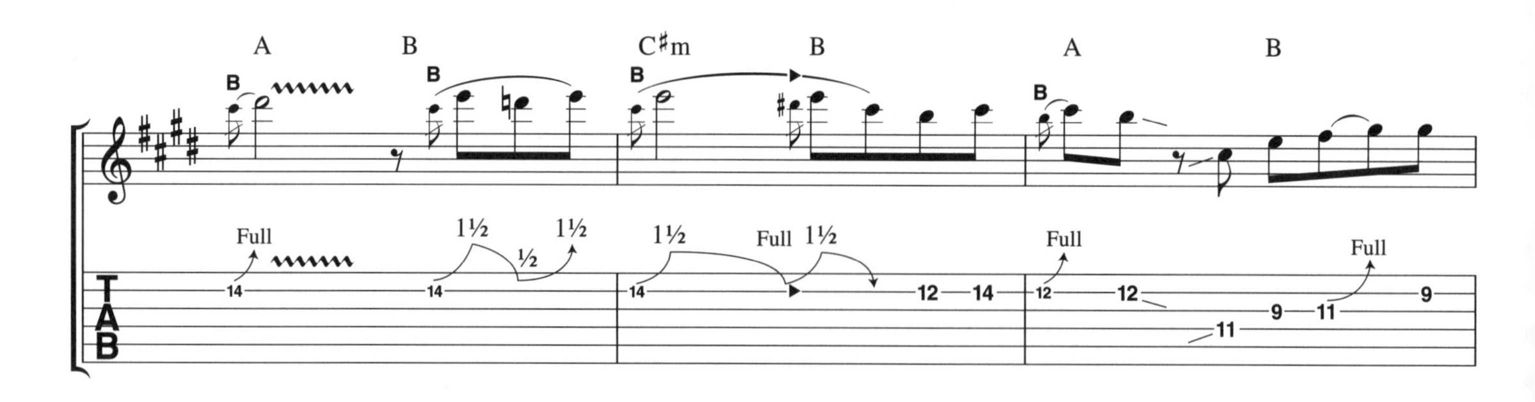
A B C♯m B A B
Full 1½ ½ 1½
TAB

Verse

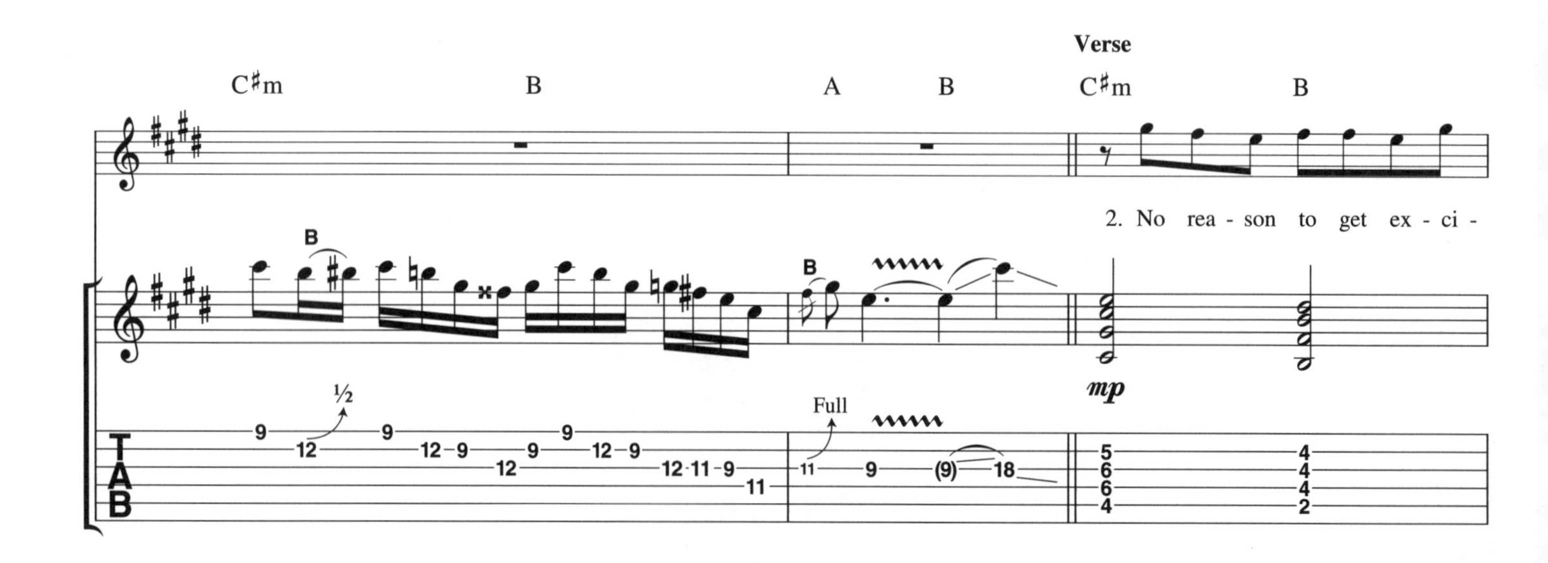
C♯m B A B C♯m B
2. No rea - son to get ex - ci -
mp
Full
TAB

A B C♯m B A B
- ted, (huh) the thief, he kind - ly spoke.
let ring
let ring
sim.
C♯m B A B C♯m B
There are man - y here a - mong us who feel that life is but a joke.
A B C♯m B A B
But you and I, we've been through that
mp
mf
let ring
C♯m B A B C♯m B
and this is not our fate. So let us not talk false -

A
B
C♯m
B
A
B
- ly now, the ho - ur's get - tin' late, oh. (Hey!)
f w/wah-wah

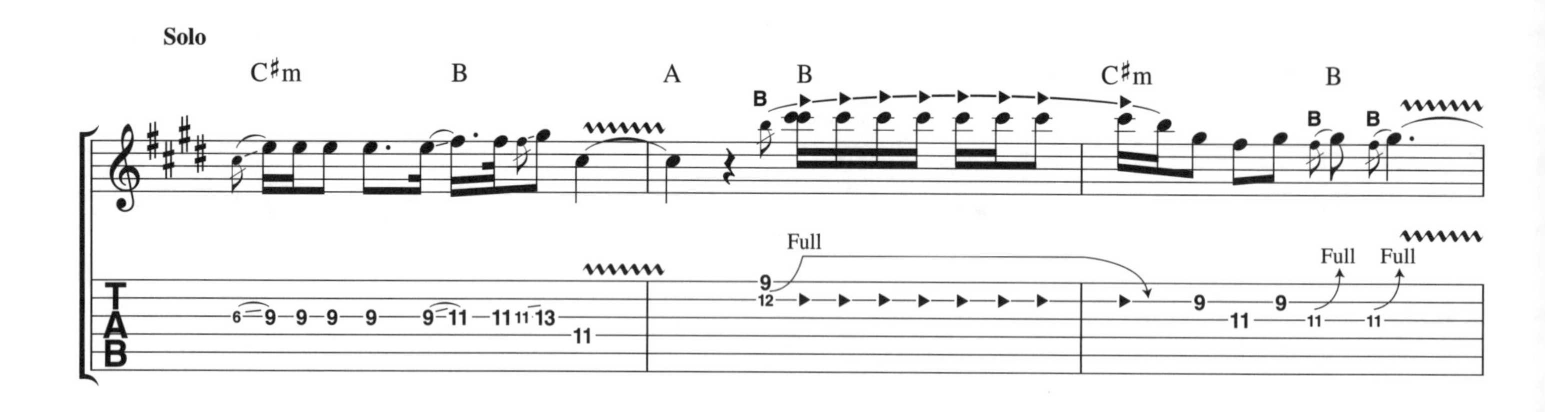
Solo
C♯m
B
A
B
C♯m
B
Full

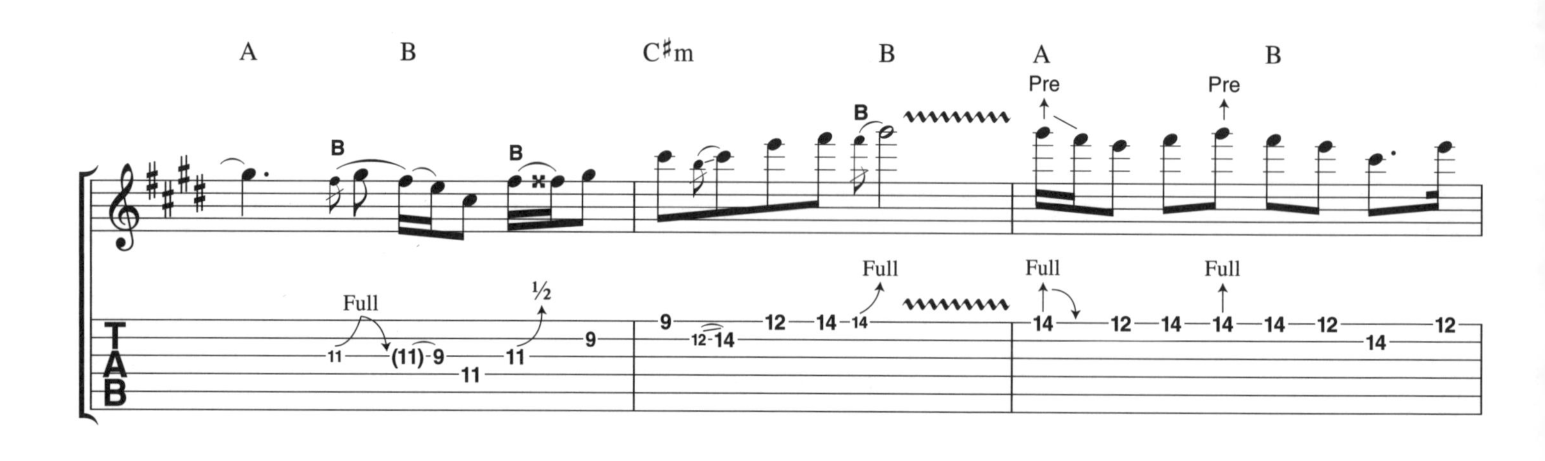
A
B
C♯m
B
A
B
Pre
Full
½

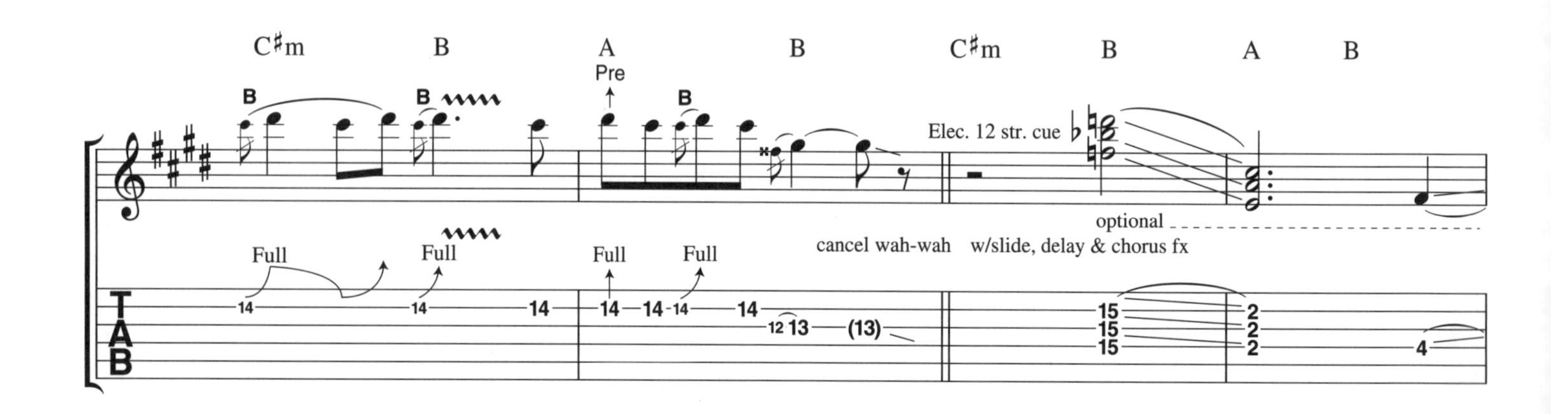
C♯m
B
A
B
C♯m
B
A
B
Pre
Full
Elec. 12 str. cue
optional
cancel wah-wah
w/slide, delay & chorus fx

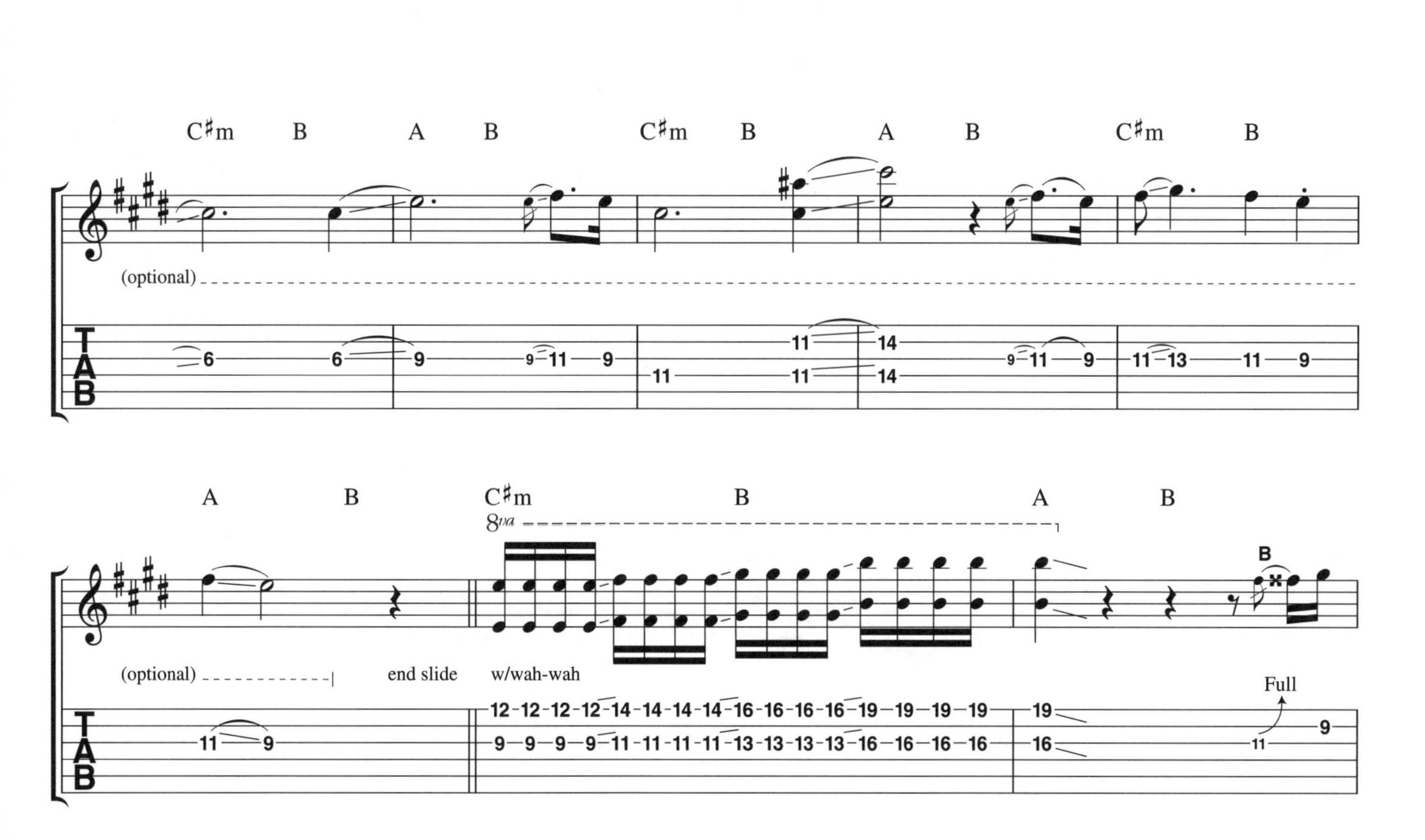
C♯m B A B C♯m B A B C♯m B
(optional)
A B C♯m B A B
8va
(optional)
end slide
w/wah-wah
Full

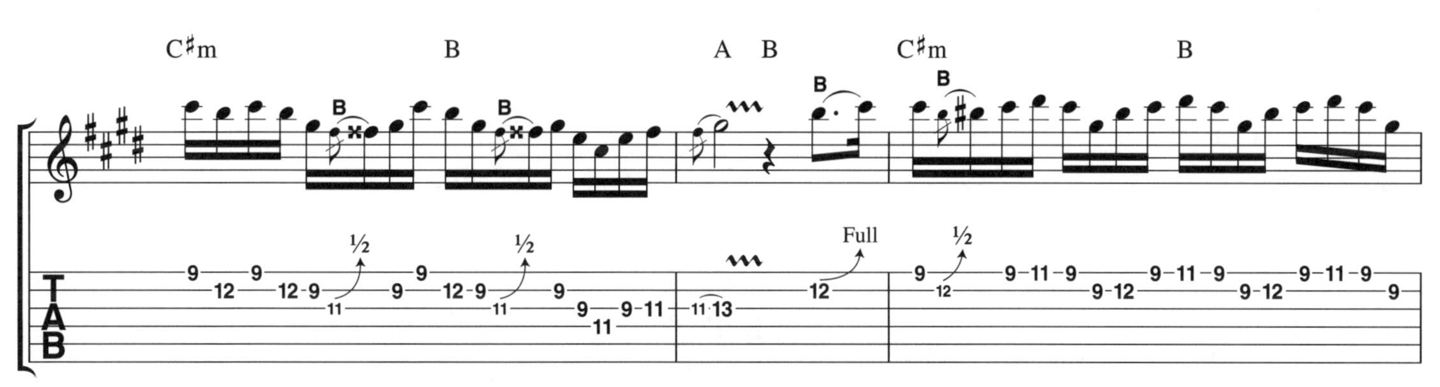
C♯m B A B C♯m B
½
Full

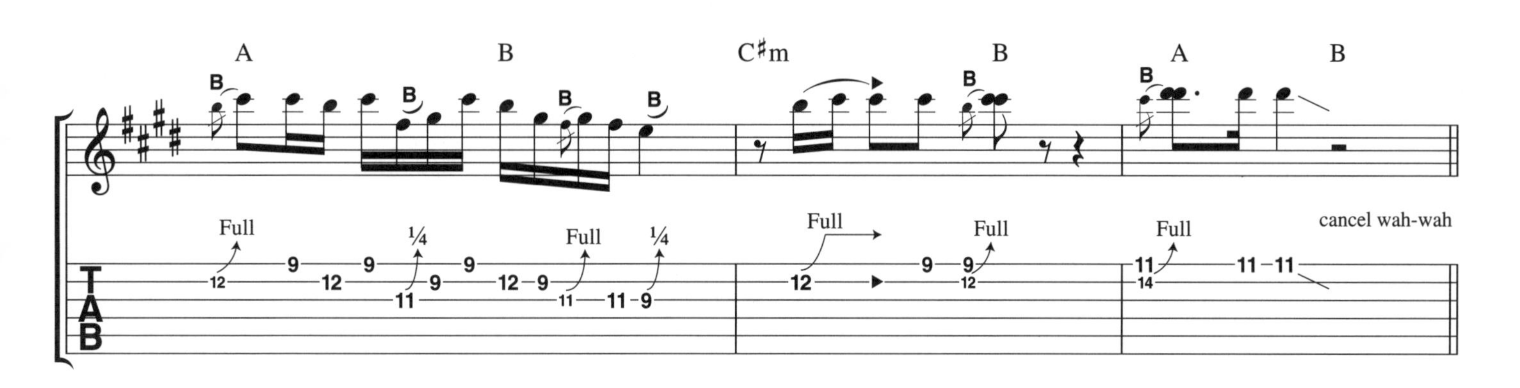
A B C♯m B A B
Full
¼
cancel wah-wah

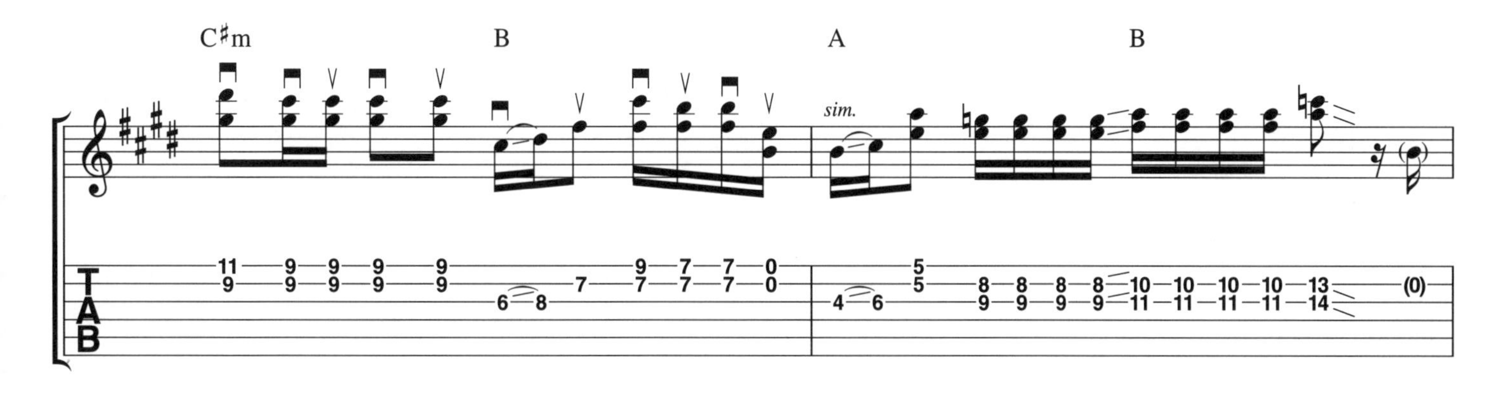
C♯m B A B
sim.

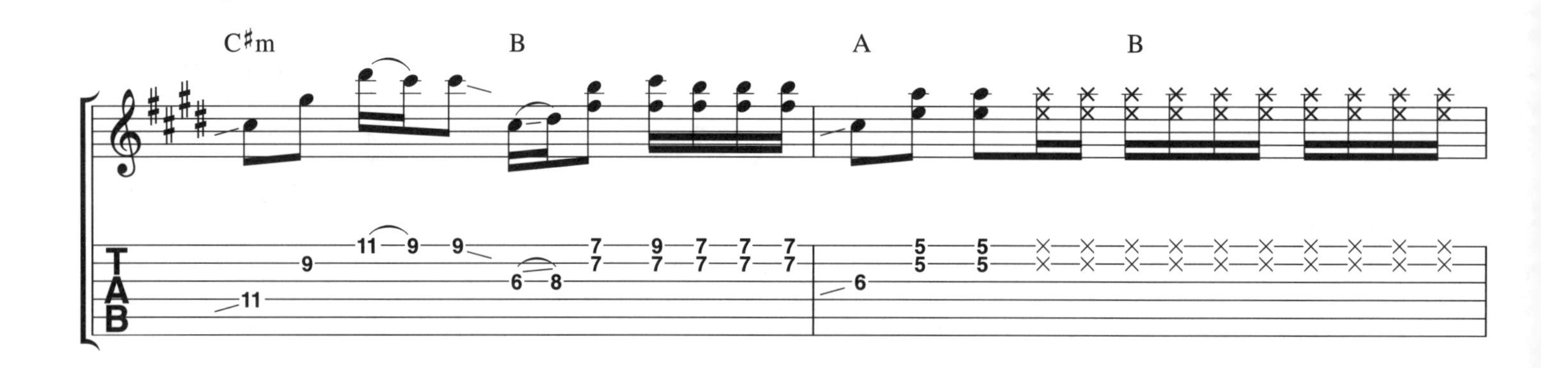
C♯m
B
A
B

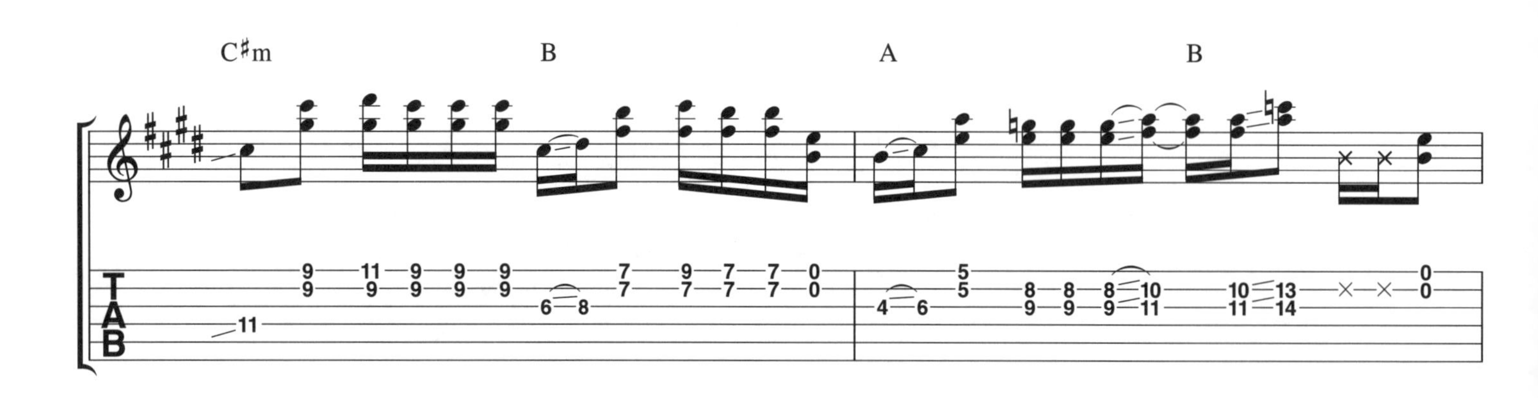
C♯m
B
A
B

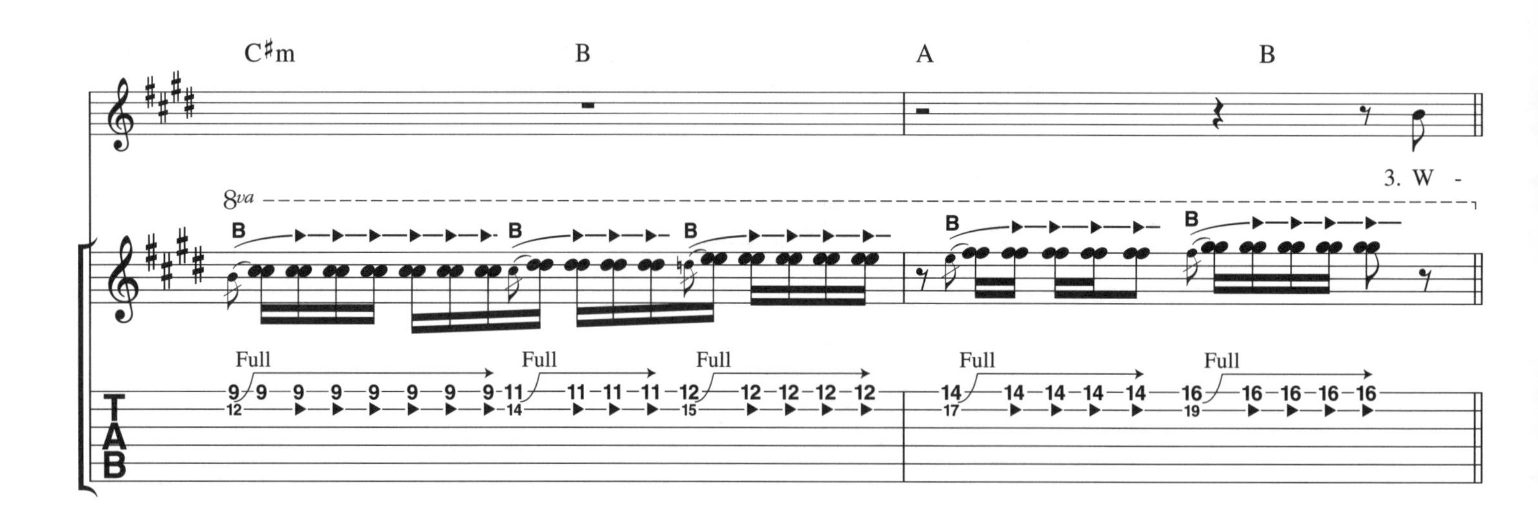
C♯m
B
A
B
3. W -
8va
Full
Full
Full
Full
Full

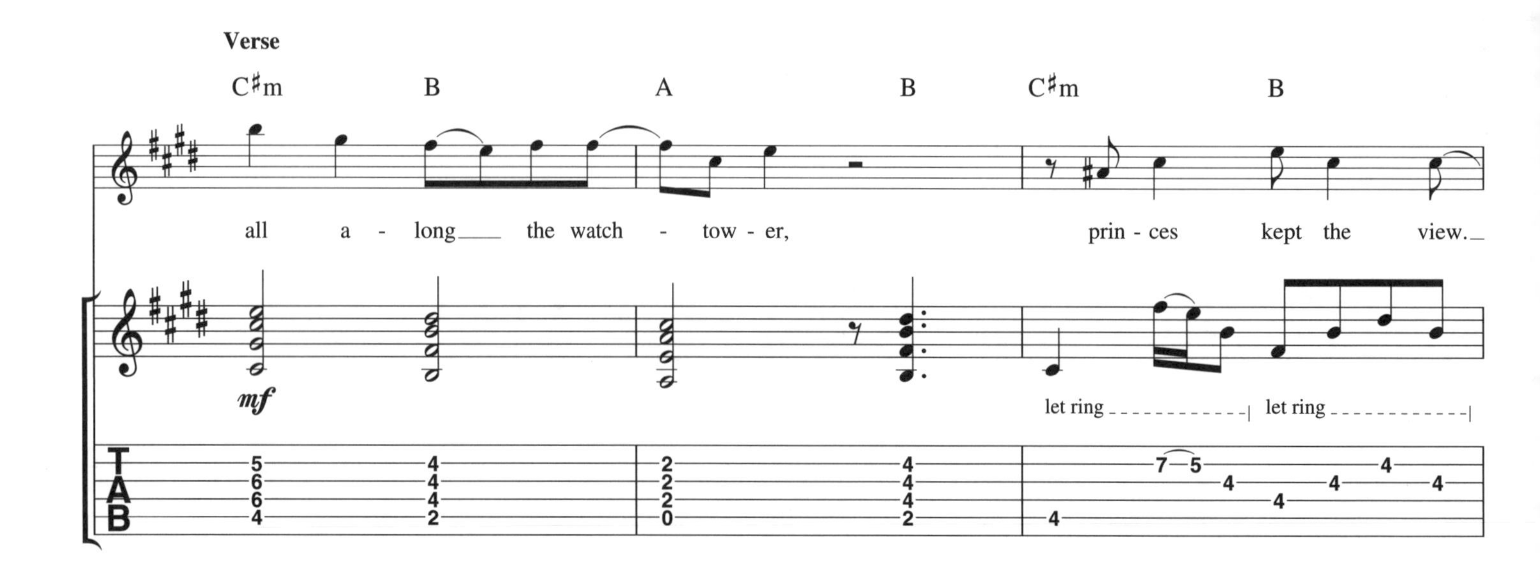
Verse
C♯m
B
A
B
C♯m
B
all a - long the watch - tow - er, prin - ces kept the view.
mf
let ring
let ring

A B C♯m B A B
While all the wo - men came and went,
C♯m B A B C♯m B
bare foot ser - vants too well ah, oh out - side in the cold
P.M.
A B C♯m B A B
dis - tance ah a wild cat did growl.
C♯m B A B
Two rid - ers were ap - proach - in' and the

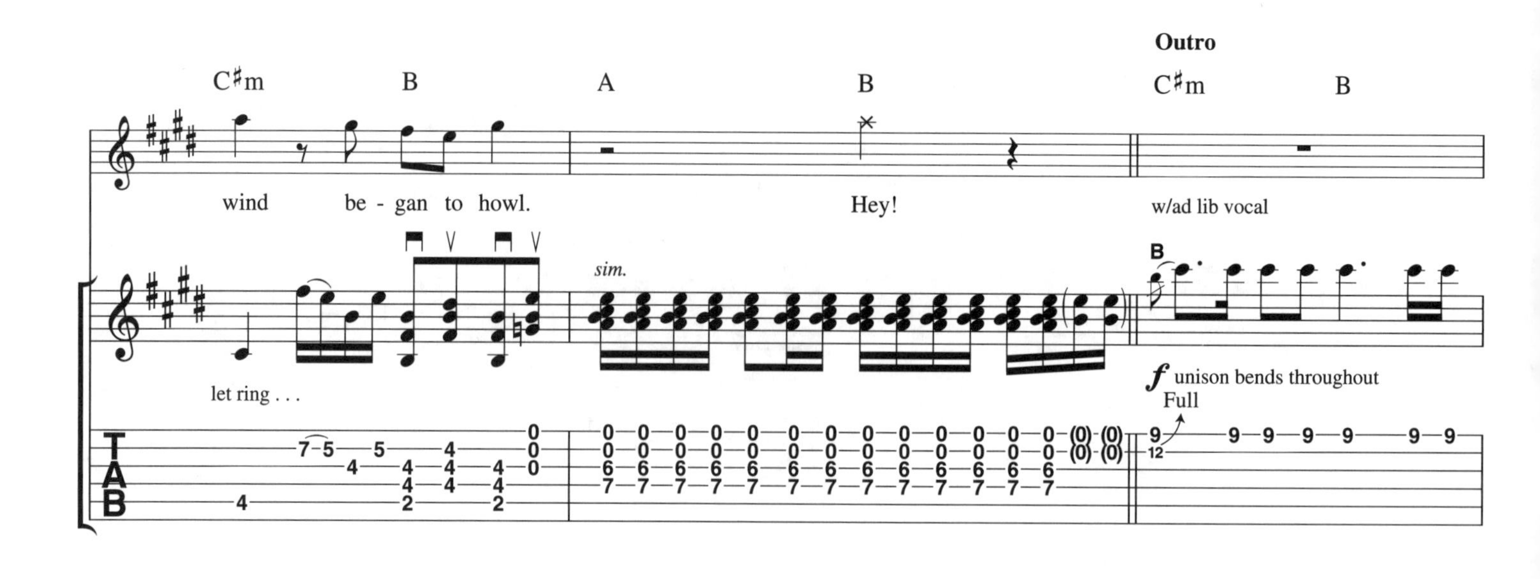
Outro
C♯m
B
A
B
C♯m
B
wind be - gan to howl.
Hey!
w/ad lib vocal
let ring . . .
sim.
unison bends throughout
Full

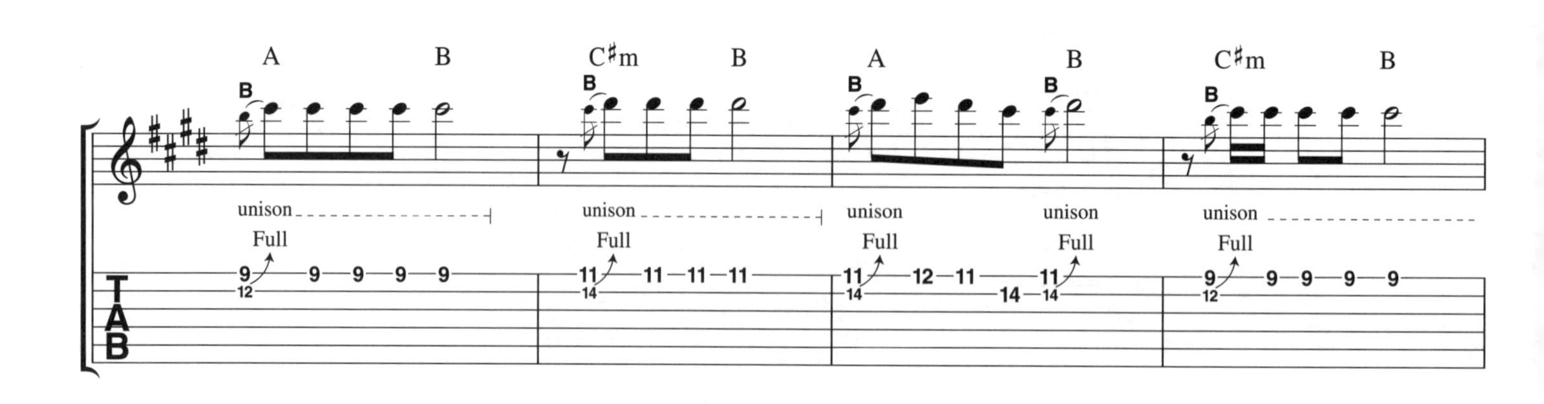
A
B
C♯m
B
A
B
C♯m
B
unison
Full

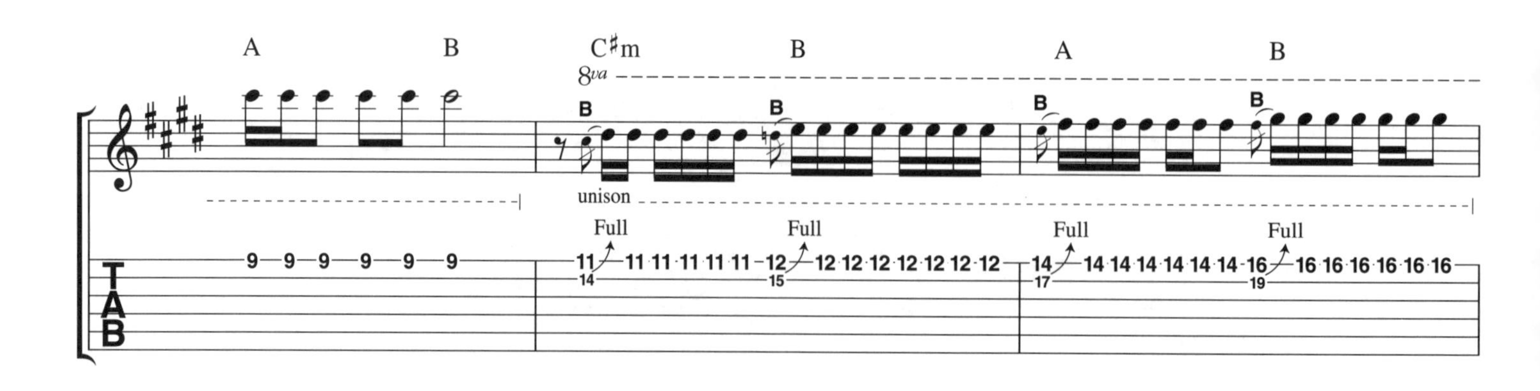
A
B
C♯m
B
A
B
8va
unison
Full

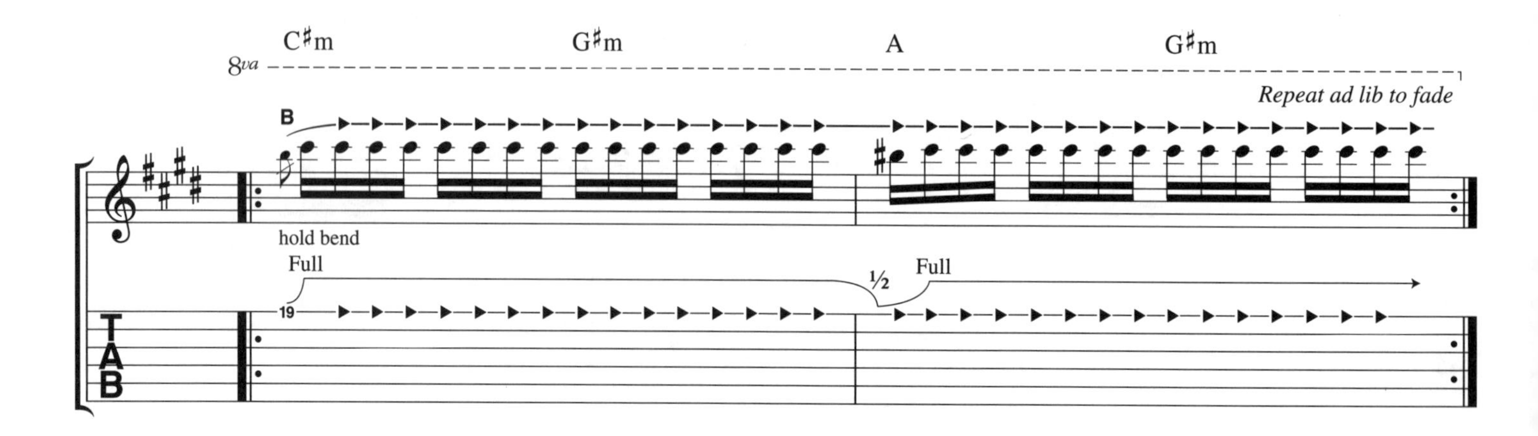
C♯m
G♯m
A
G♯m
8va
Repeat ad lib to fade
hold bend
Full
½

born to be wild

Words & Music by Mars Bonfire

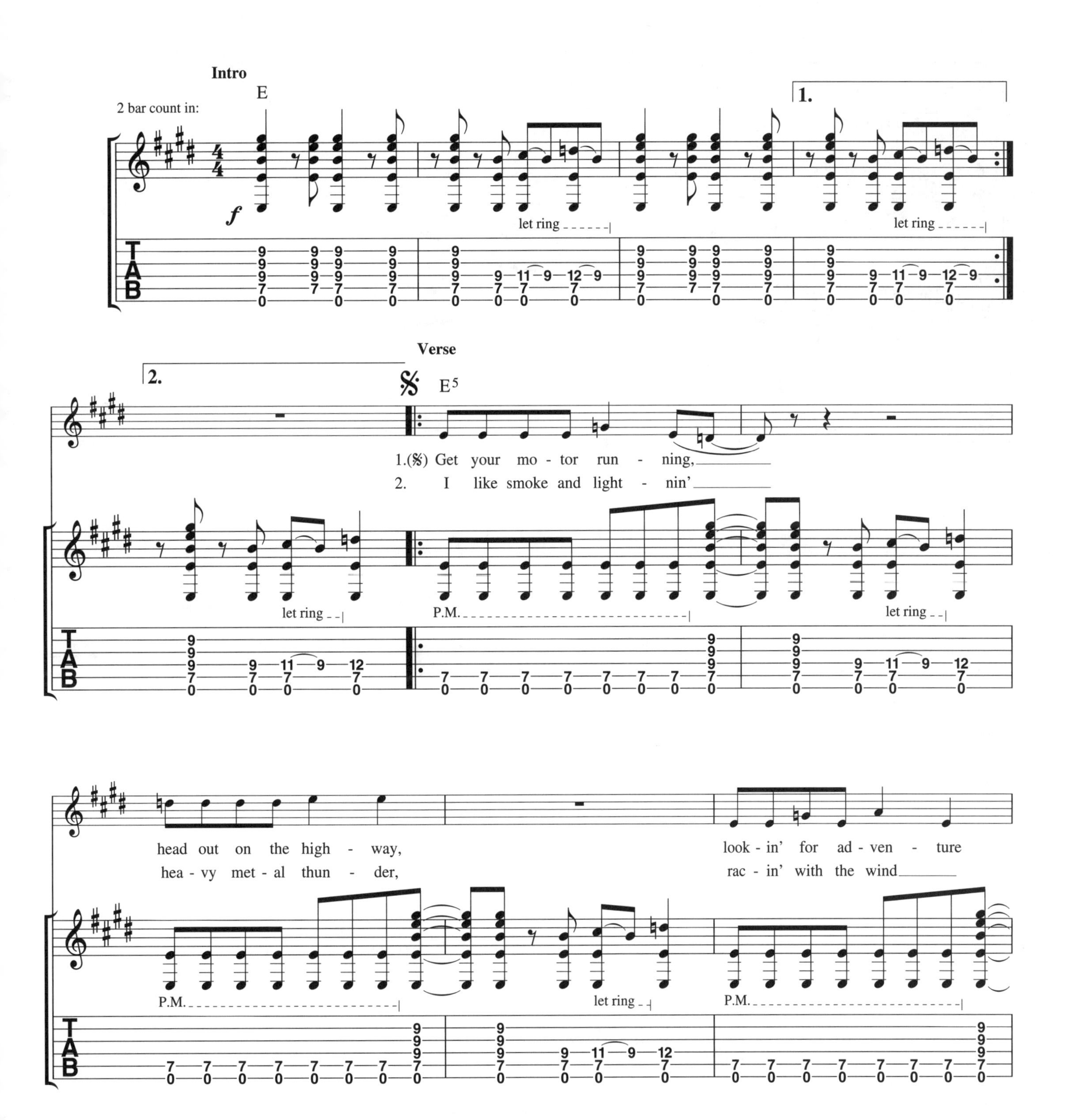

and what - ev - er comes our way.
and the feel - in' that I'm un - der.
let ring
P.M.
let ring
Pre-chorus
G A E G A
Yeah, dar - lin' go make it hap - pen, take the world in a
B
let ring
let ring
2° & 3° w/Fill 1
½
let ring
let ring
E G A E
love em - brace. Fire all of your guns at once and
B
2° w/Fill 2, 3° w/Fill 4
Full
let ring
let ring
2° w/Fill 3, 3° w/Fill 5
Fill 1
E
B
½

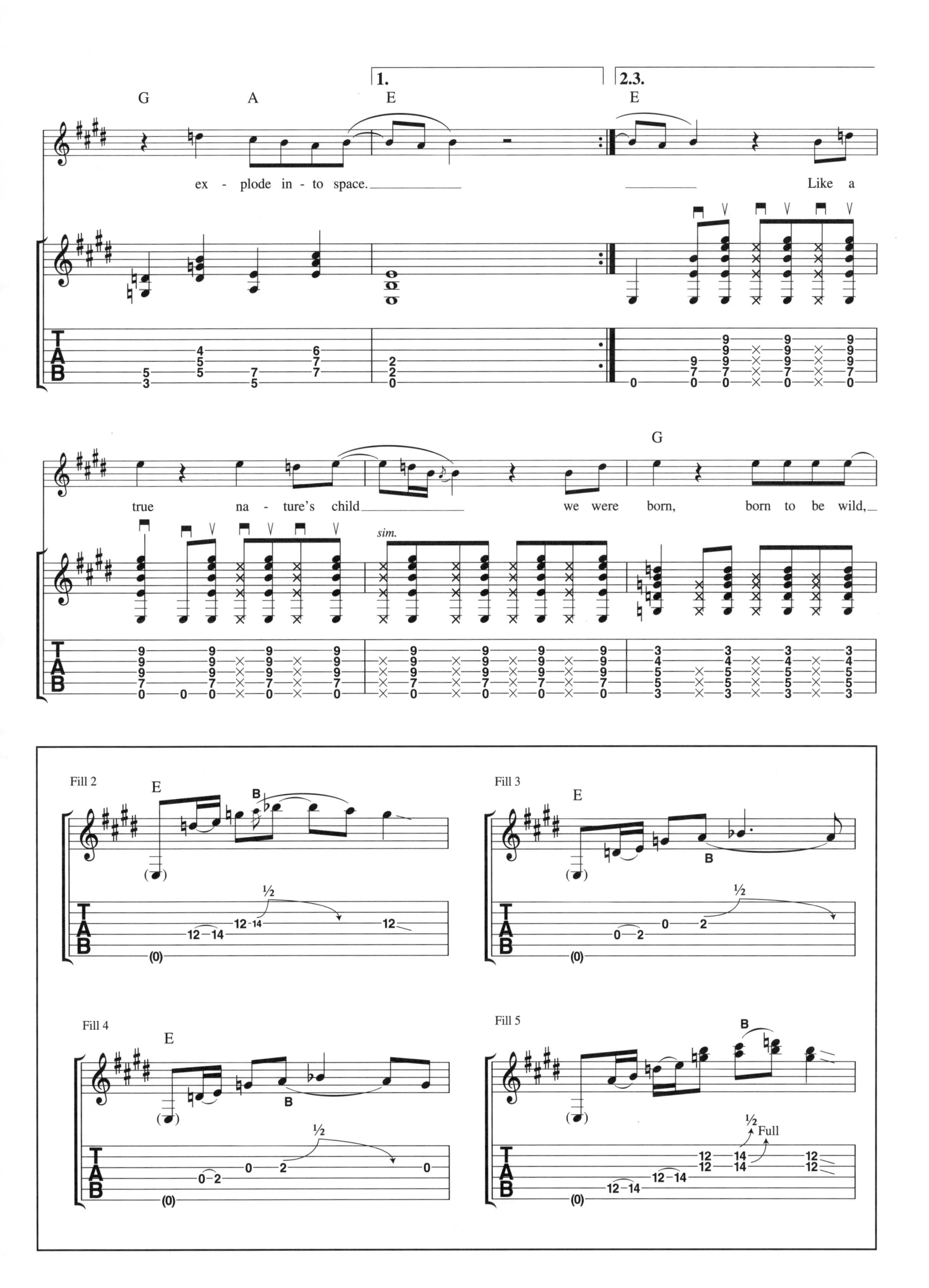
1.
2.3.
G
A
E
E
ex - plode in - to space.
Like a
true na - ture's child
we were born, born to be wild,
G
sim.
Fill 2
E
B
½
Fill 3
E
B
½
Fill 4
E
B
½
Fill 5
B
½
Full

A
G
we can climb so high,
I nev - er wan - na
TAB
Chorus
E5
E5
(D5)
E5
die.
Born to be wild.
mp
D5
E5
(D5)
E5
D5
To Coda
Organ solo
E
Born to be wild.
1.
2.

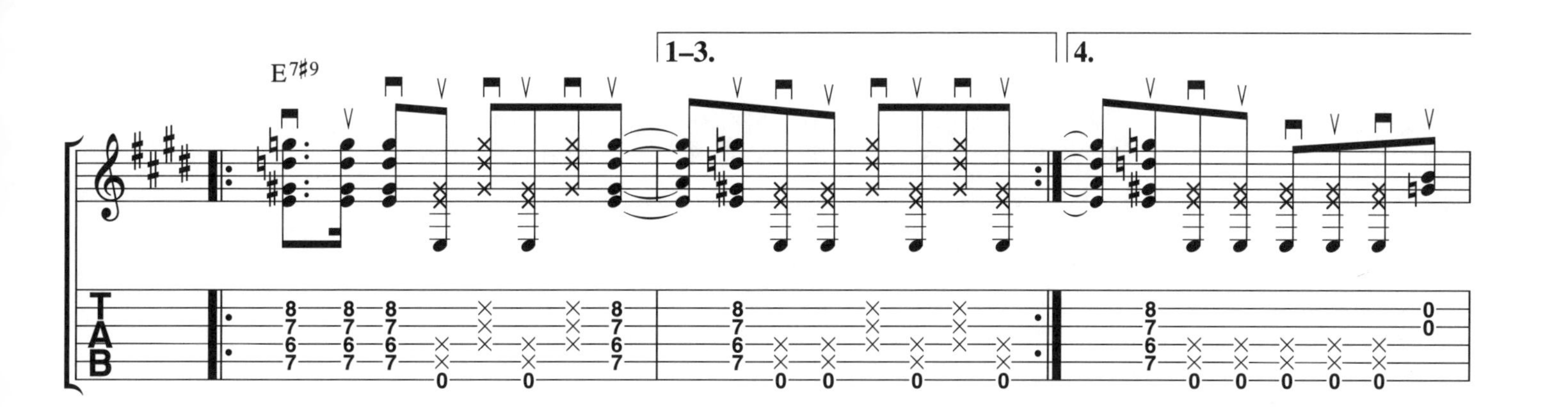
E7♯9
1–3.
4.

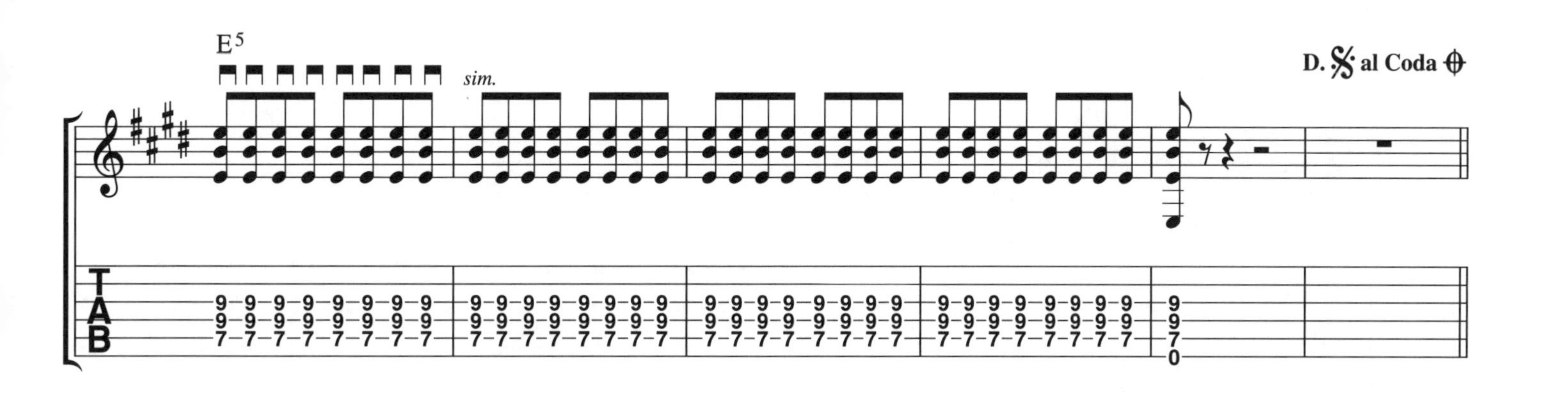
E5
sim.
D.S. al Coda

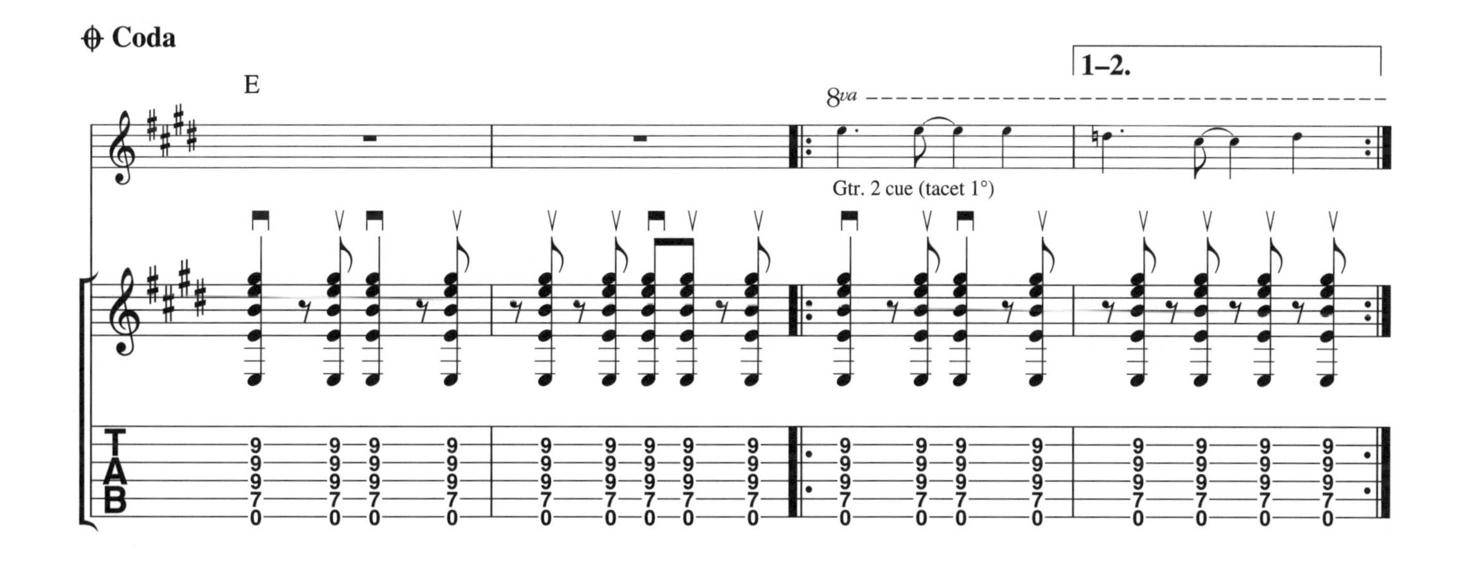
Coda
E
1–2.
8va
Gtr. 2 cue (tacet 1°)

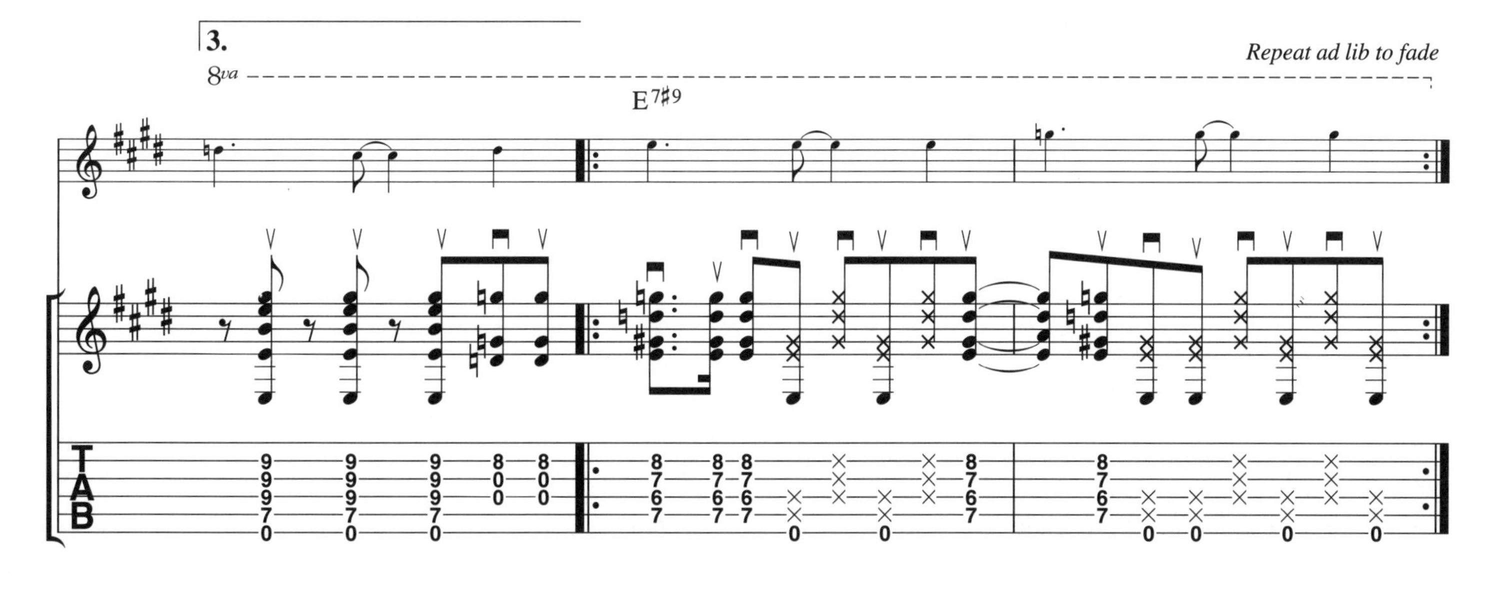
3.
8va
Repeat ad lib to fade
E7♯9

back in the ussr

Words & Music by John Lennon & Paul McCartney

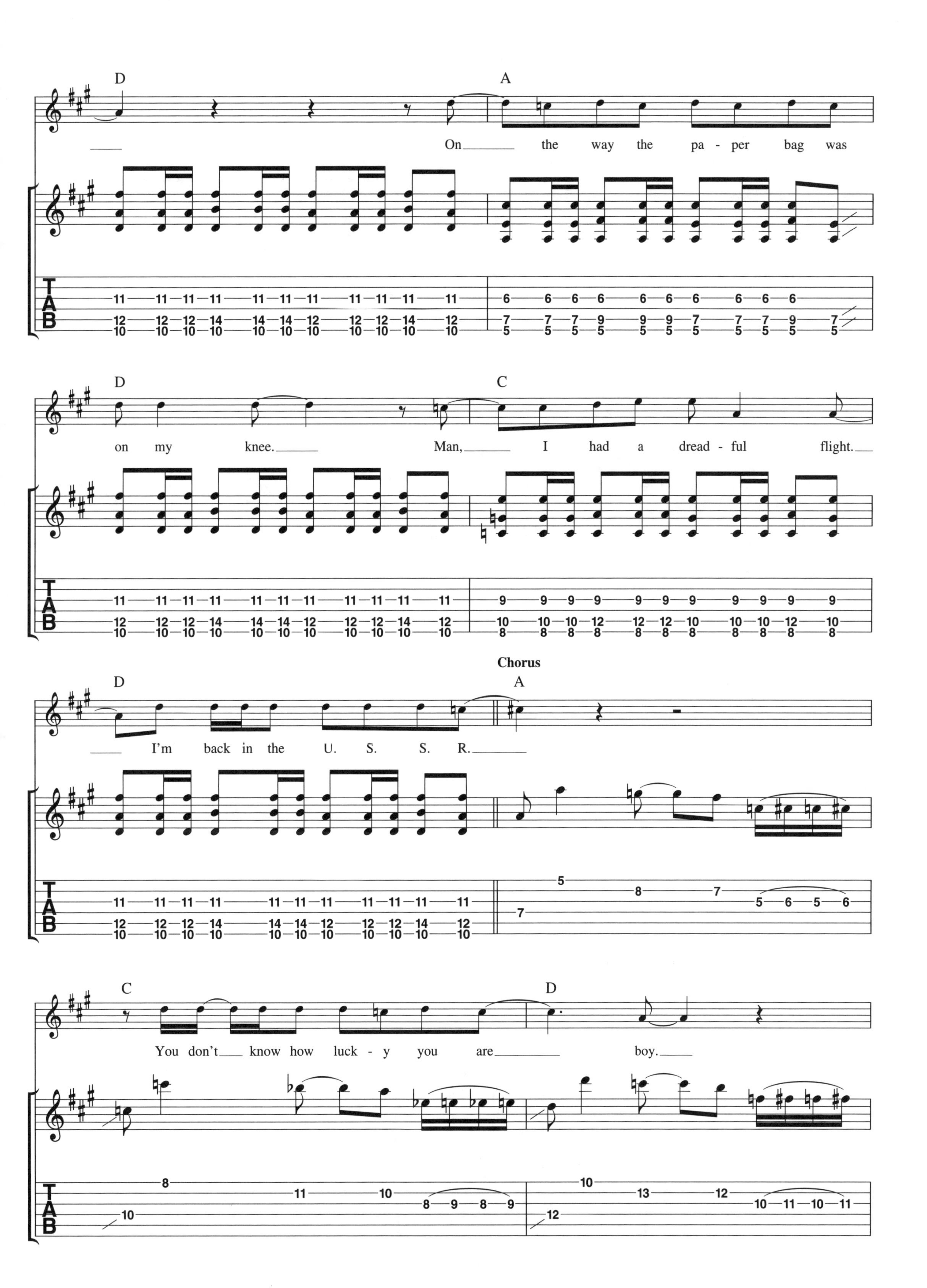
D
A
On the way the pa - per bag was
D
C
on my knee. Man, I had a dread - ful flight.
Chorus
D
A
I'm back in the U. S. S. R.
C
D
You don't know how luck - y you are boy.

D7
A
Back in the U. S. S. R.
B
E7
A
Been a - way so long I hard - ly
D
C
knew the place.
Gee, it's good to be back home.
D
A
Leave it 'til to - mor - row to un -

D
C
pack my case. Hon - ey, dis - con - nect the phone.
Chorus
D
A
I'm back in the U. S. S. R.
C
D
You don't know how luck - y you are boy.
N.C.
Back in the U. S., back in the U. S., back in the U. S. S. R.

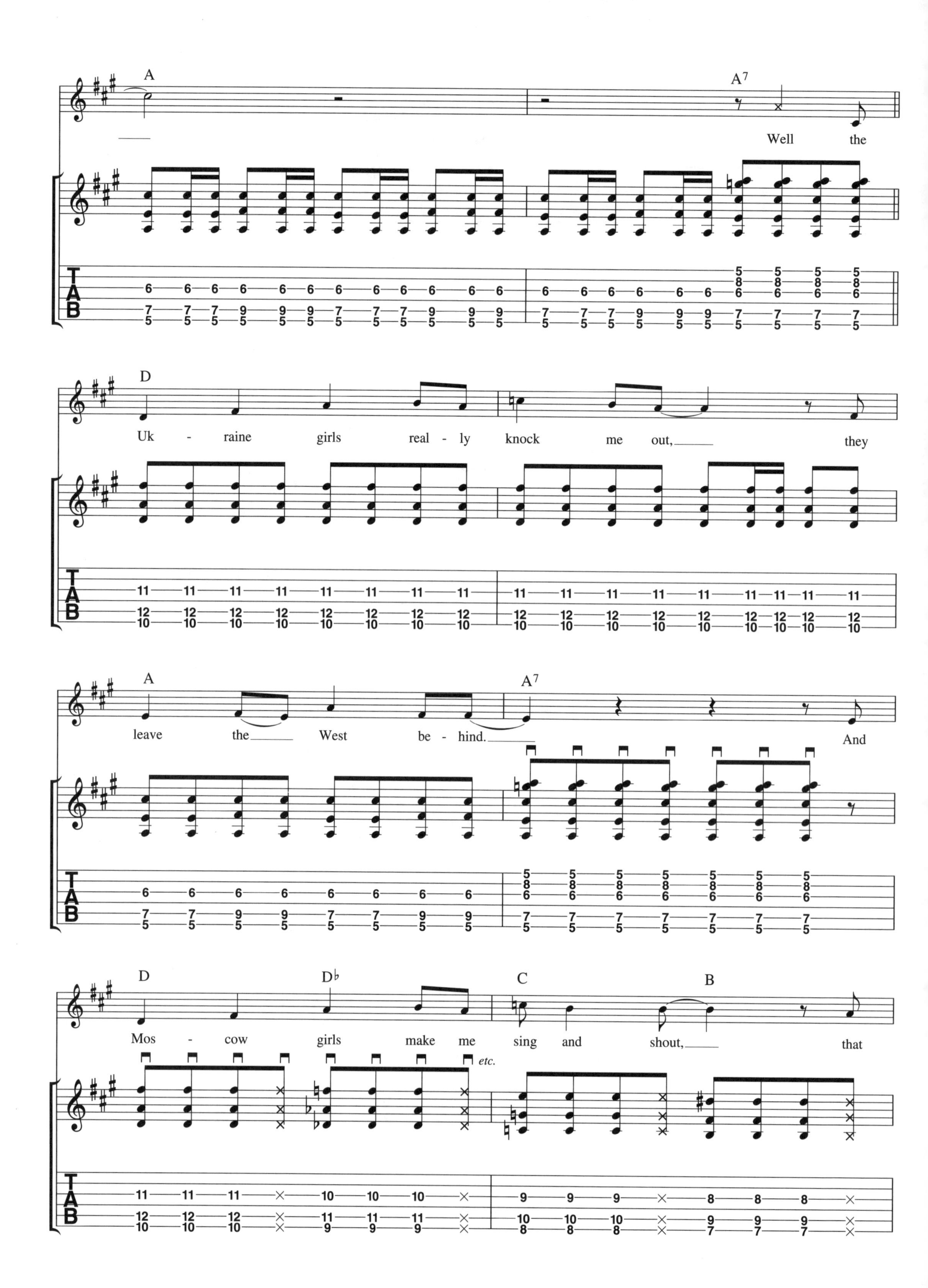
A
A7
Well the
D
Uk - raine girls real - ly knock me out,
they
A
leave the West be - hind.
A7
And
D
Db
Mos - cow girls make me sing and shout,
etc.
C
B
that
TAB

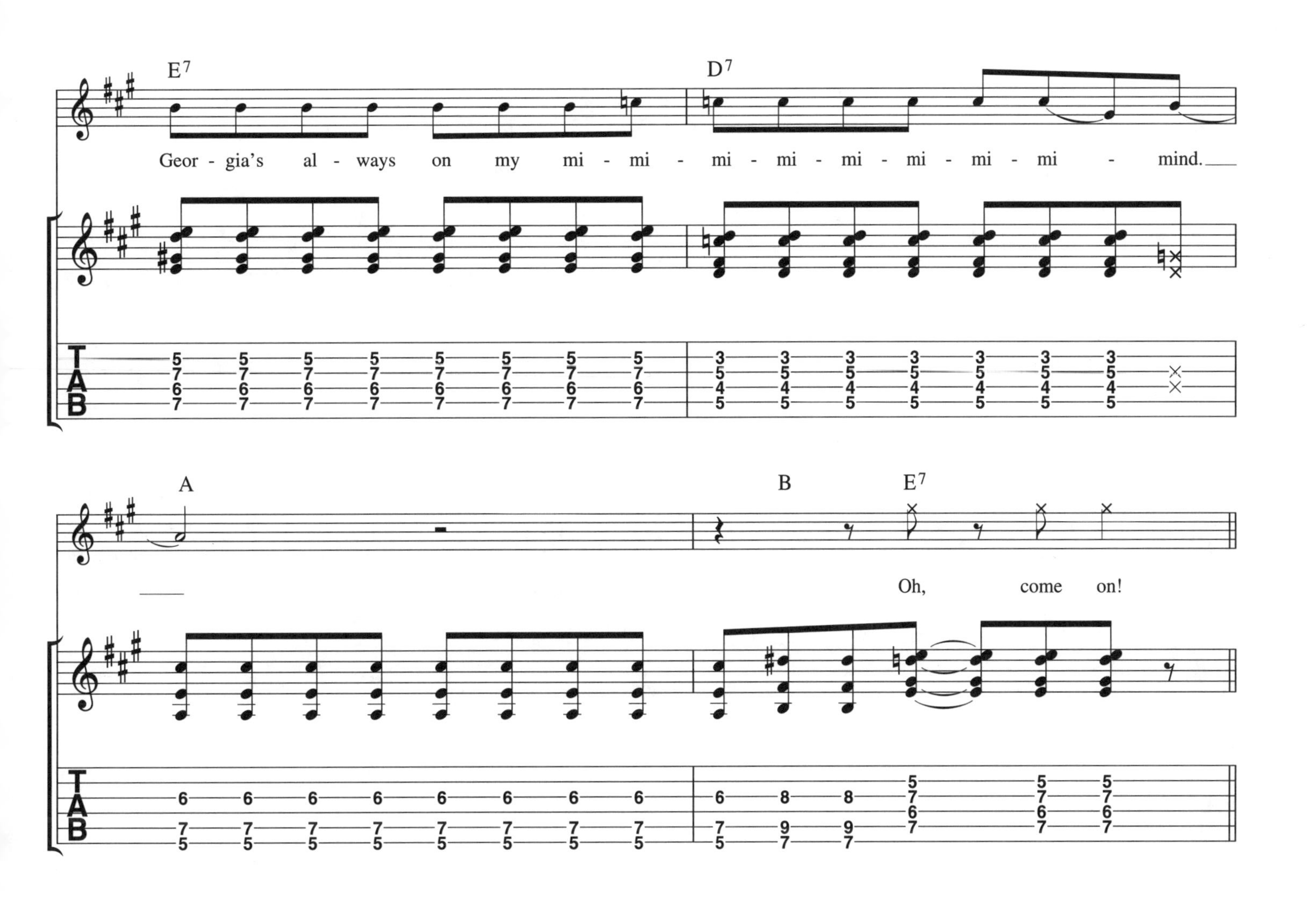
E7
D7
Geor - gia's al - ways on my mi - mi - mi - mi - mi - mi - mi - mi - mind.
A
B
E7
Oh, come on!

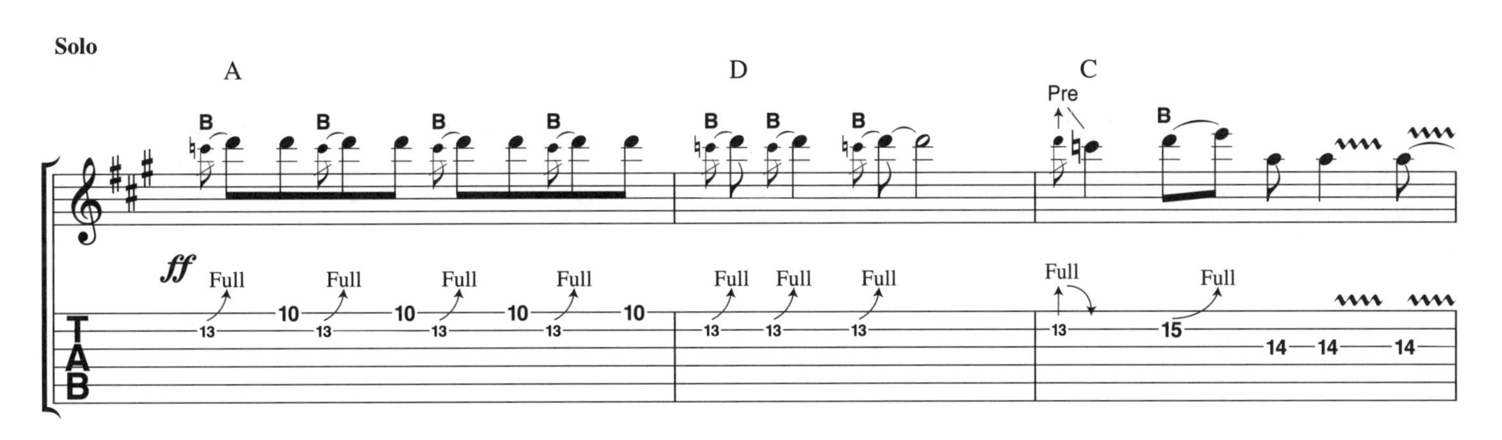
Solo
A
D
C
Pre
Full

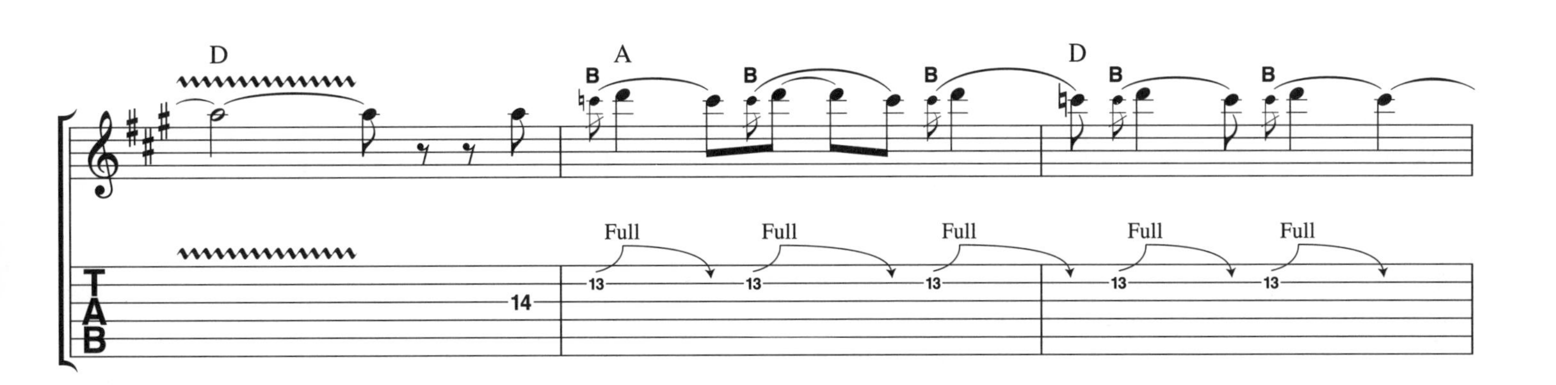
D
A
D
Full

Chorus
C
D
A
I'm back in the U. S. S. R.,
Full
¼
you don't know how luck - y you are, boys.
Back in the U. S. S. R.
A
A7
Well, the
D
Uk - raine girls real - ly knock me out, they

A
A7
leave the West be - hind. And
D
D♭
C
B
Mos - cow girls make me sing and shout, that
etc.
E7
D7
Geor - gia's al - ways on my mi - mi - mi - mi - mi - mi - mi - mi - mind.
A
B
E7
Oh, 3. Show

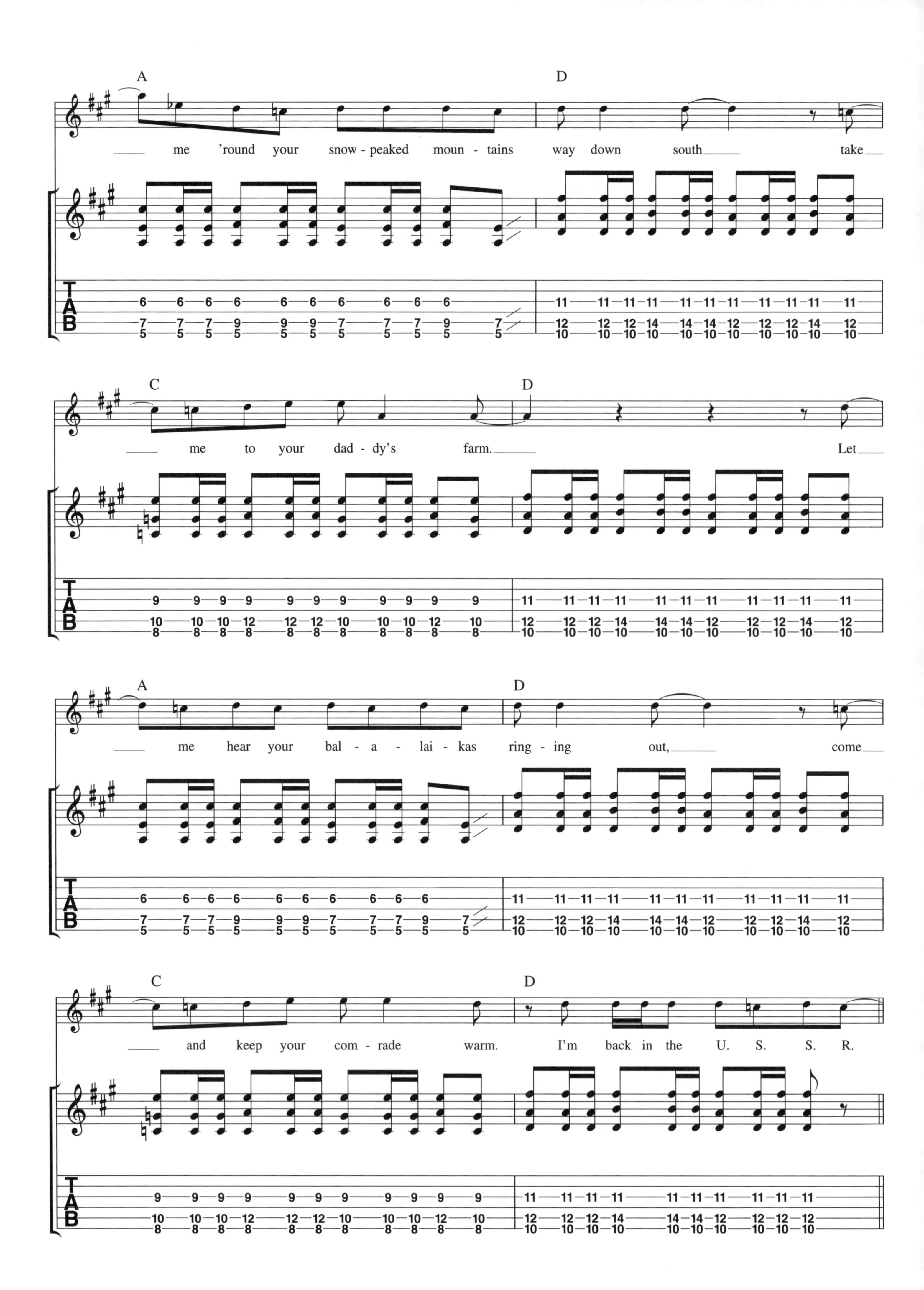
A
D
me 'round your snow-peaked moun-tains way down south take
C
D
me to your dad-dy's farm. Let
A
D
me hear your bal-a-lai-kas ring-ing out, come
C
D
and keep your com-rade warm. I'm back in the U. S. S. R.
TAB
TAB
TAB
TAB

A
C
Hey!
You don't know how luck - y you are,
D
D7
boys.
Back in the U. S. S. R.
A
B
E7
Oh,
let me tell you hon - ey!
Outro
A
Play three times
Ooh.
Ooh, ooh, ooh.
Vocal 2° only

Words & Music by John Lennon & Paul McCartney

C♯m
young - er so much young - er than to - day,
when I was young I nev - er
etc.
F♯m
D G A
I nev - er need - ed an - y - bod - y's help in an - y way.
need
A
But now those days are gone I'm
Now these days are gone.
C♯m
F♯m
not so self as - sured,
And now I find
now I find I've

D G A
changed my mind and op - ened up the doors.
Chorus
Bm
Help me if you can I'm feel - in' down,
G
And I do ap - pre - ci - ate you be - ing round.
E
Help me get my feet

Verse 2

And now my life has changed in oh, so many ways
My independence seems to vanish in the haze
But every now and then I feel so insecure
I know I just need you like I've never done before.

i can see for miles

Words & Music by Pete Townshend

Chorus
E5
I can see for
G6
miles and
A
miles and
C
miles and
D add9
miles and
E
miles,
oh yeah.
To Coda
Verse
E
G5
A
E
2. If you think that I don't know a-bout the lit-tle tricks you play.
3. You took ad-van-tage of my trust in you when I was so far a-way.
Play 1°
Play 2°
TAB

G5 A5 E5 G5 A
And nev - er see you when de - lib - 'rate - ly you put things
I saw you hold - ing lots of other guys and now you've got the
E A5
in my way.
nerve to say:
Well here's a poke at you, you're gon - na
that you still want me well

B
A5
B5
choke on it too, you're gon - na lose that smile, be - cause all the while.
that's as may - be but you got - ta stand trial be - cause all the while.
I can see for
mp
Chorus
A
E
A
E
miles and miles, I can see for miles and miles, I can see for
f
G6
A
C
D add9
miles and miles and miles and miles and
1.
E
miles, oh, yeah.
let ring . . .

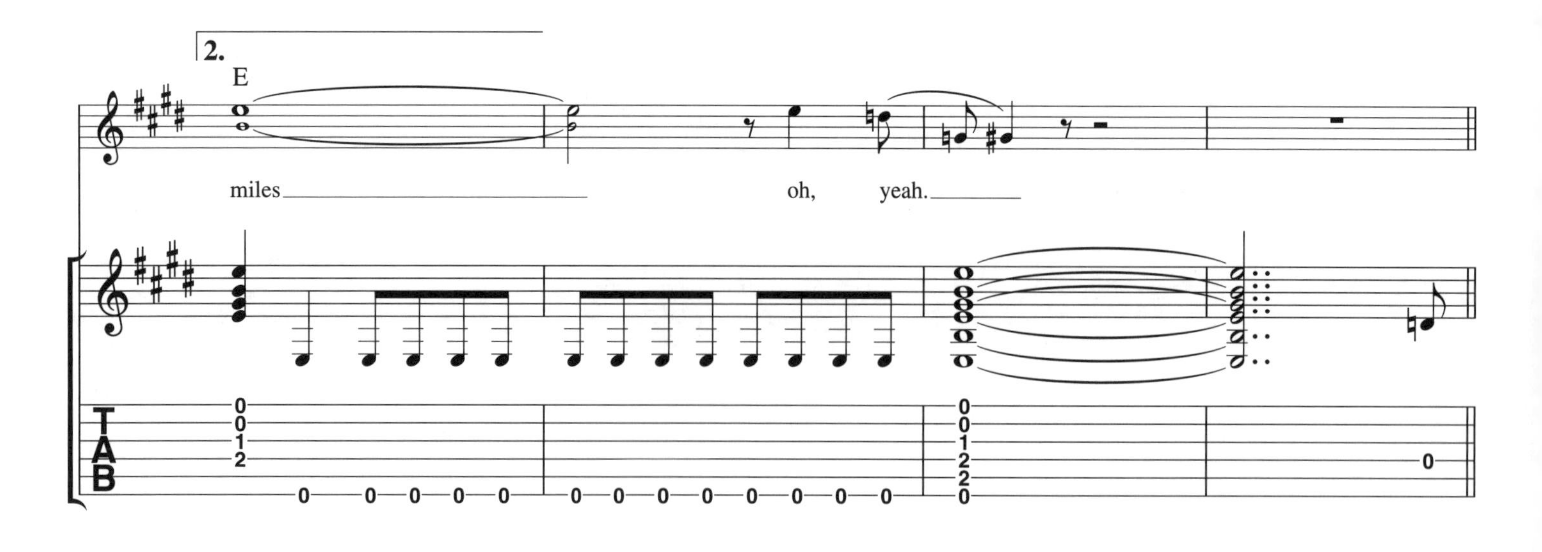
2.
E
miles
oh,
yeah.
TAB

Solo

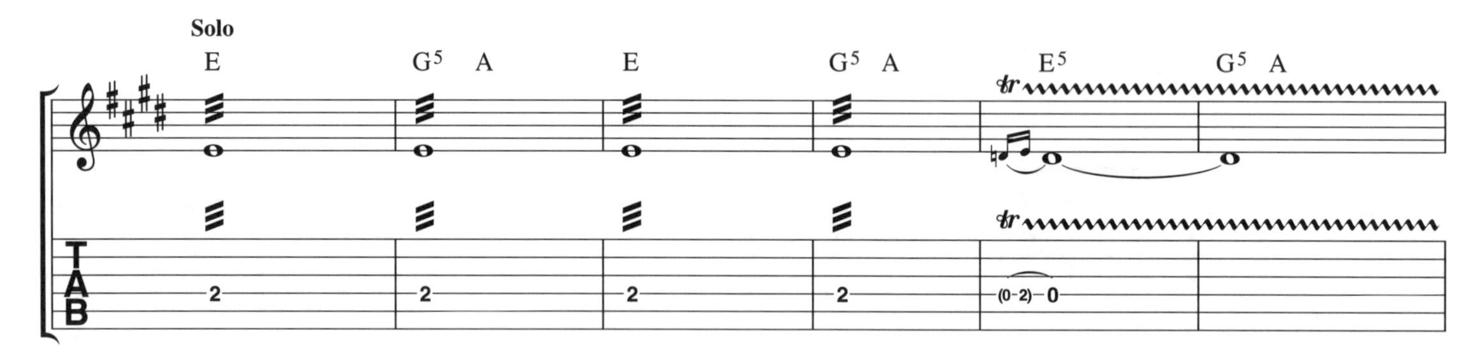
E
G5
A
E
G5
A
E5
G5
A
tr
TAB

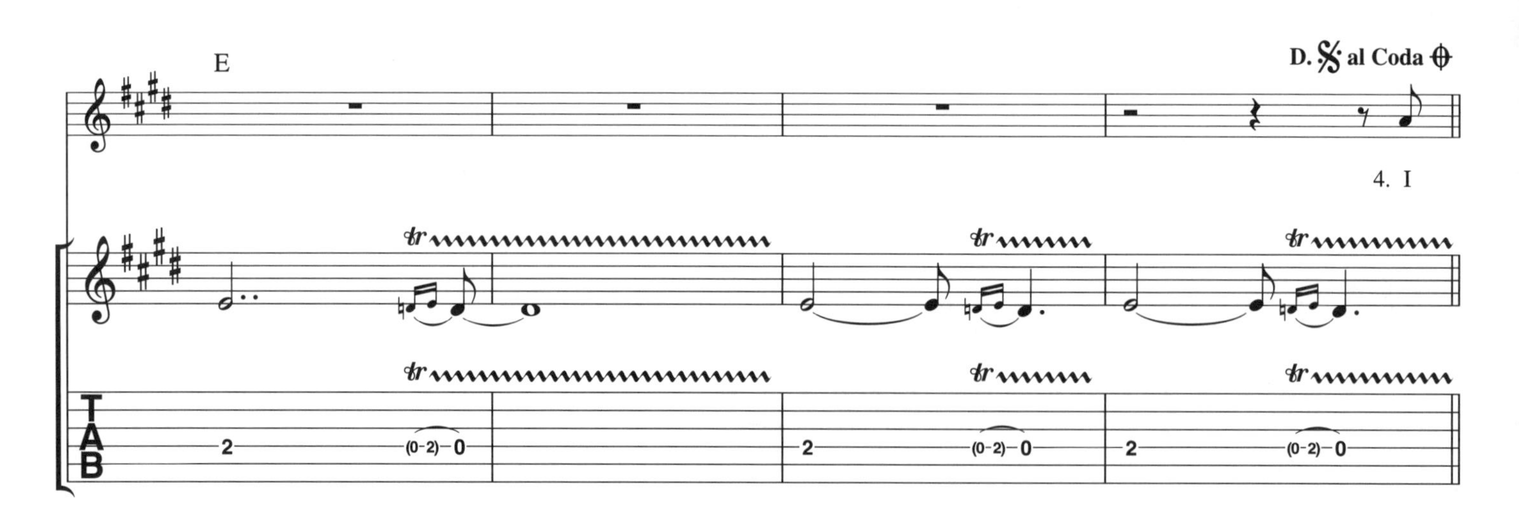
E
D.S. al Coda
4. I
tr
TAB

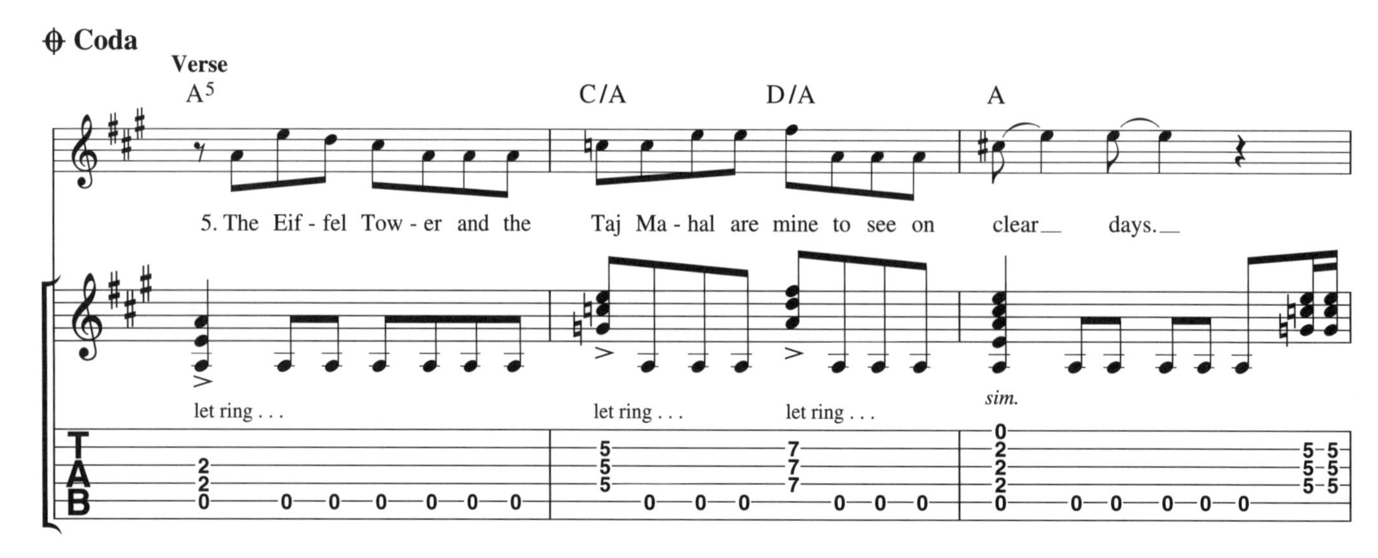
Coda
Verse
A5
C/A
D/A
A
5. The Eif - fel Tow - er and the
Taj Ma - hal are mine to see on
clear days.
let ring . . .
let ring . . .
let ring . . .
sim.
TAB

C D A C D
You thought that I would need a crys - tal ball to see right
A D
through the haze. Well here's a poke at you, you're gon - na
E5 D E5
choke on it too. You're gon - na lose that smile, be - cause all the while,
Chorus
D A
I can see for miles and miles. I can see for

D A C/A D/A
miles and miles. I can see for miles and miles and
F/A G/A
miles and miles and miles and miles and
A5 Asus4 A A5 Asus4 A A5 Asus4 A
miles and miles.
A5 D A
Repeat to fade
I can see for miles and miles. I can see for

not fade away

Words & Music by Charles Hardin & Norman Petty

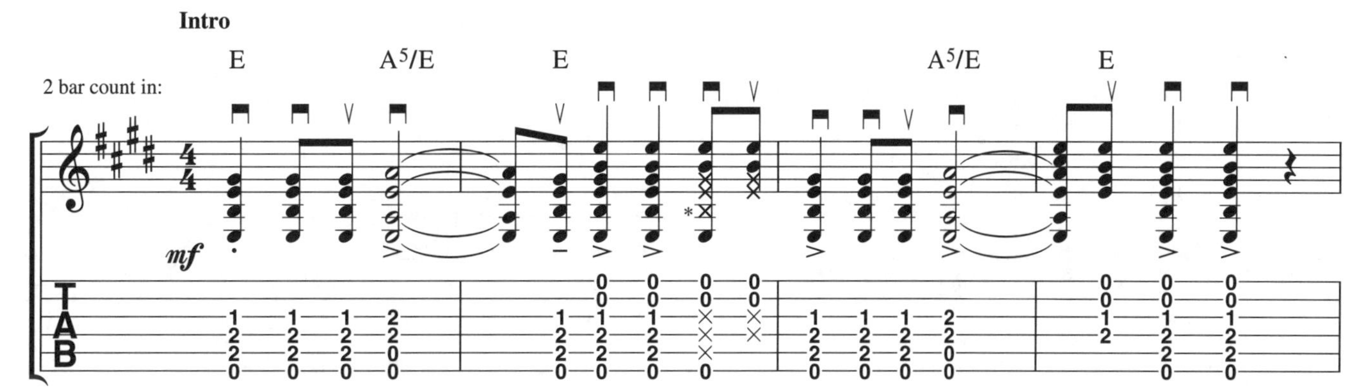

* × = release fretted string to give percussive feel

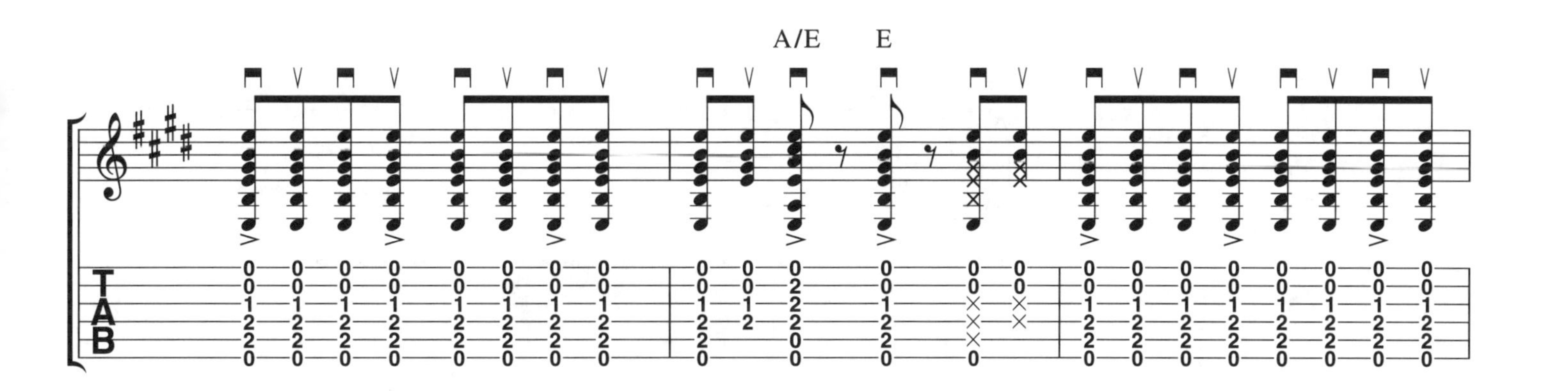

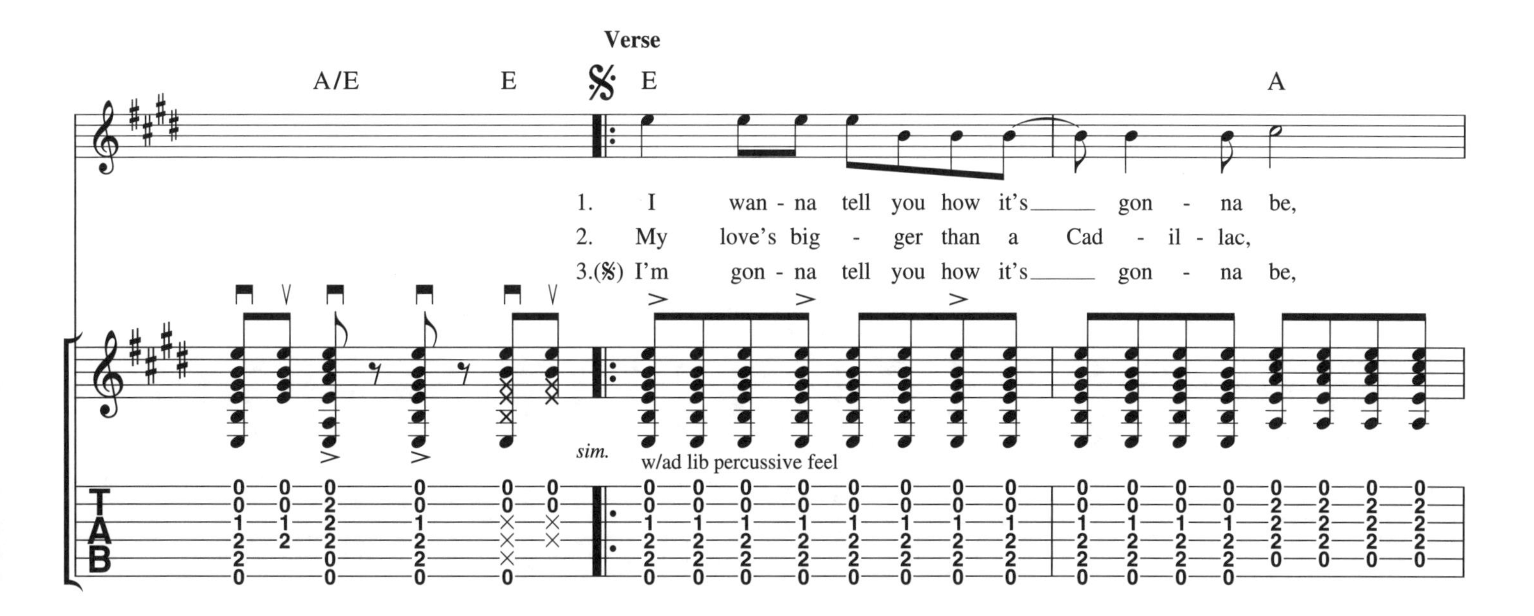

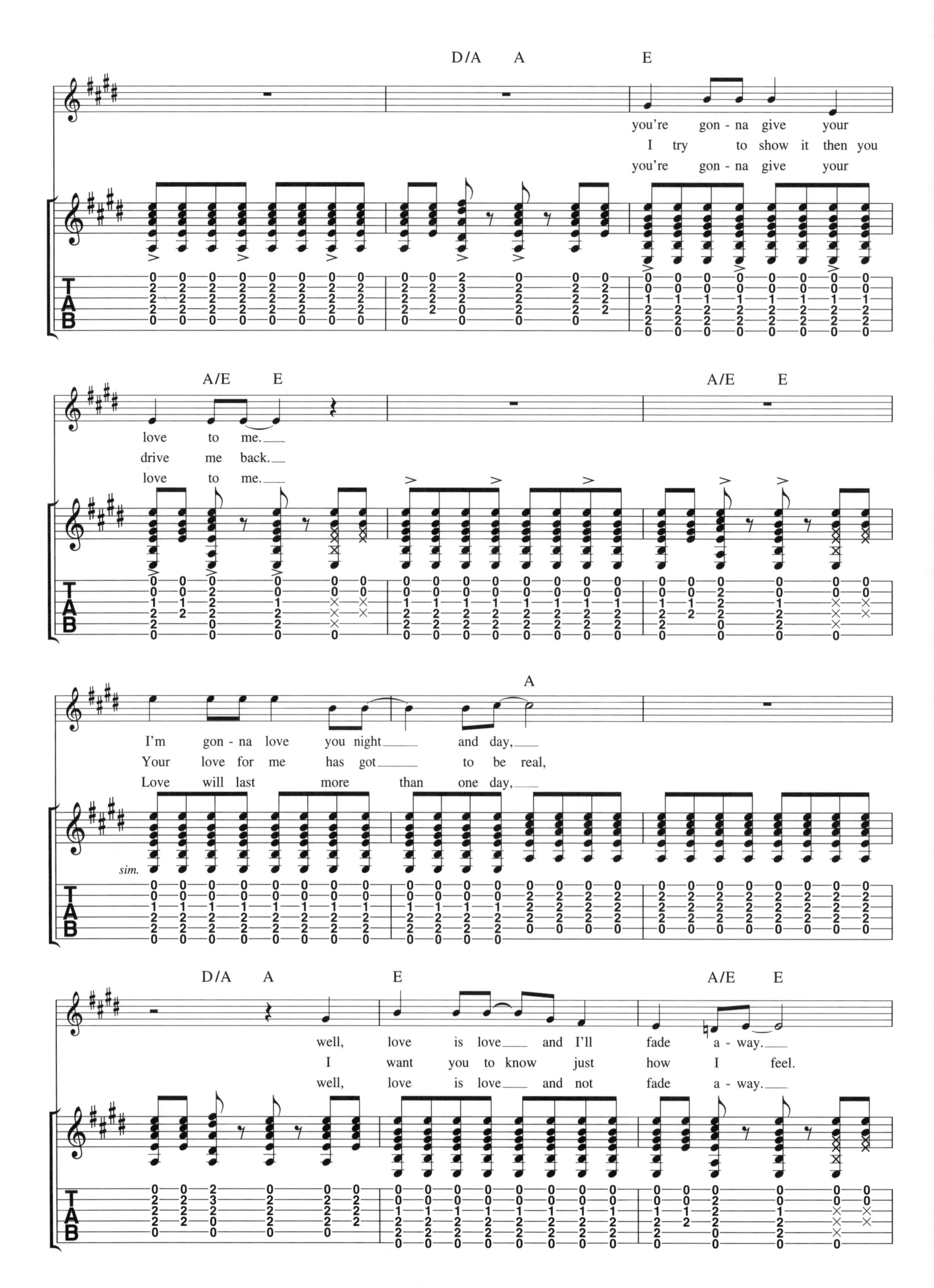
D/A A E
you're gon - na give your
I try to show it then you
you're gon - na give your
A/E E
love to me.
drive me back.
love to me.
A/E E
sim.
A
I'm gon - na love you night and day,
Your love for me has got to be real,
Love will last more than one day,
D/A A E
A/E E
well, love is love and I'll fade a - way.
I want you to know just how I feel.
well, love is love and not fade a - way.

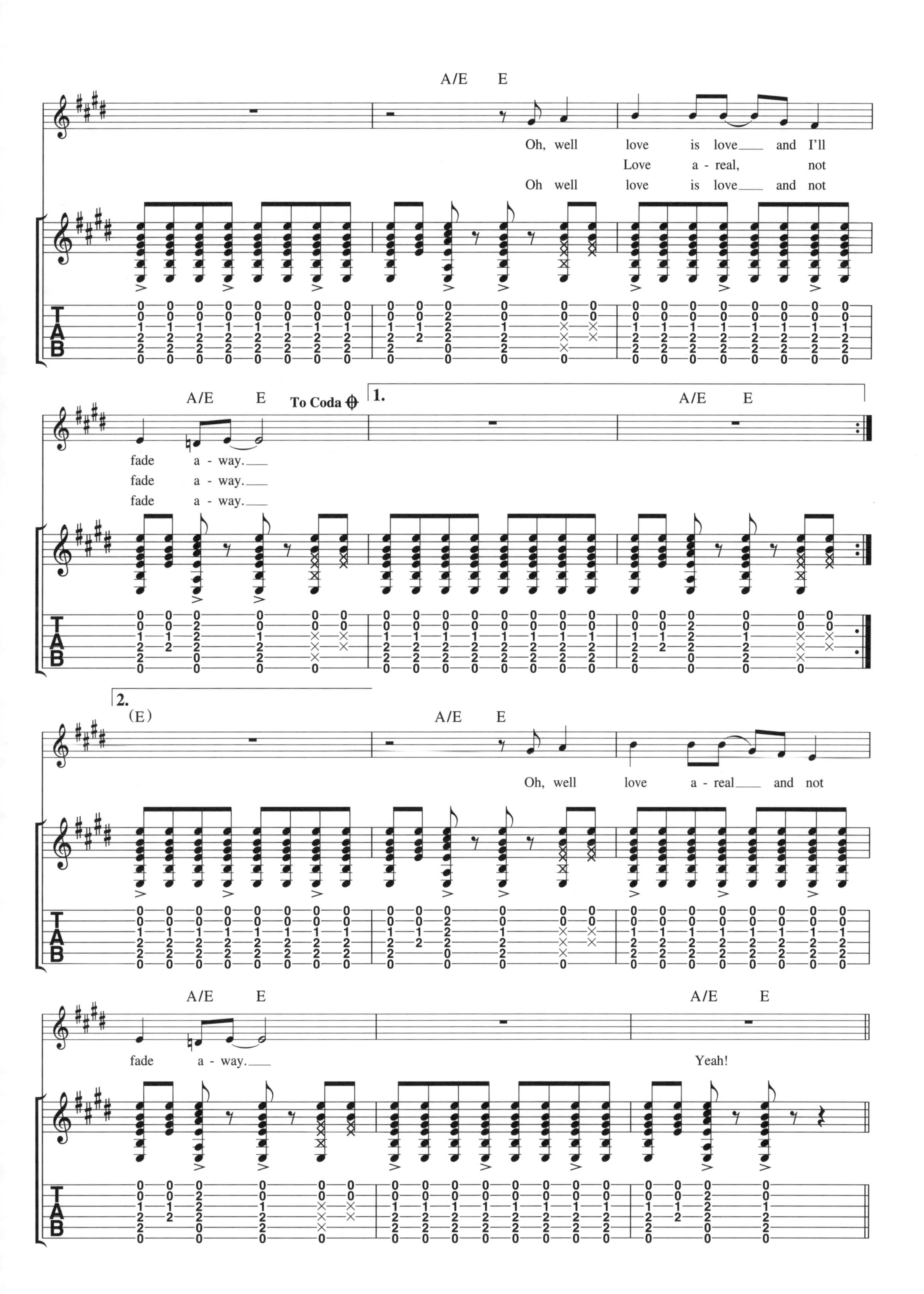
A/E
E
Oh, well love is love and I'll
Love a - real, not
Oh well love is love and not
fade a - way.
fade a - way.
fade a - way.
To Coda
1.
2.
(E)
Oh, well love a - real and not
fade a - way.
Yeah!
TAB

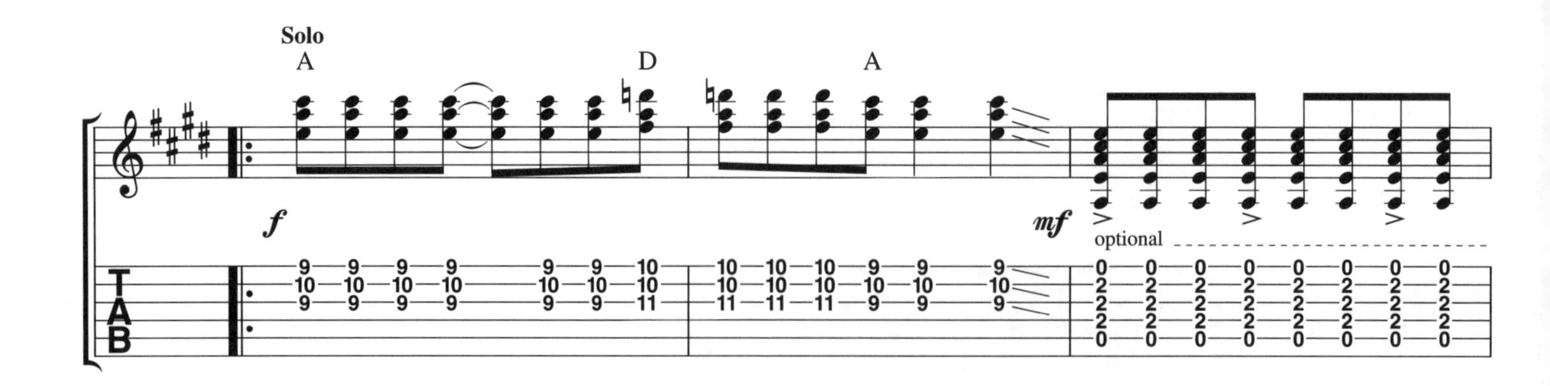
Solo
A
D
A
f
mf
optional
TAB

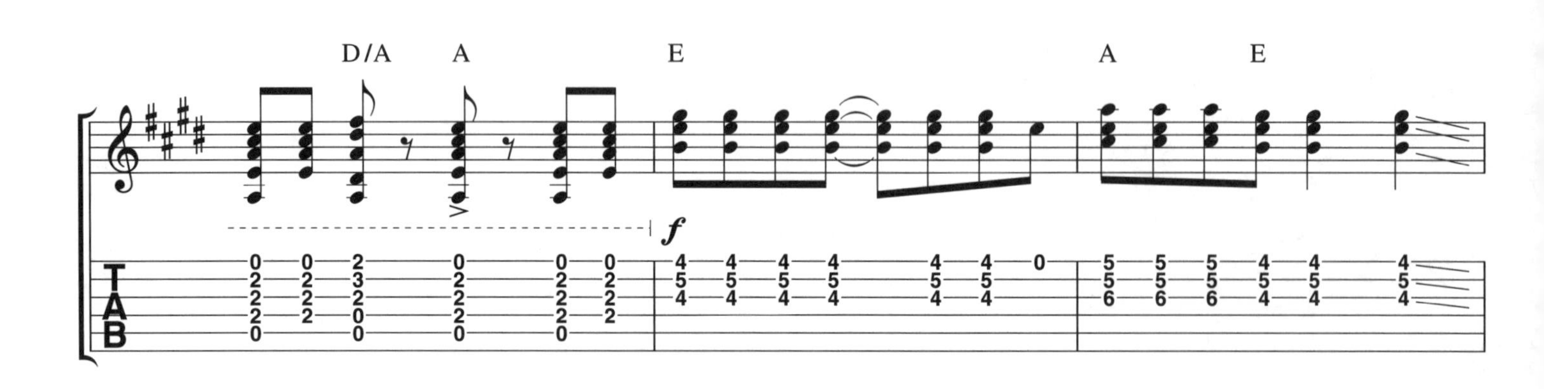
D/A
A
E
A
E
f
TAB

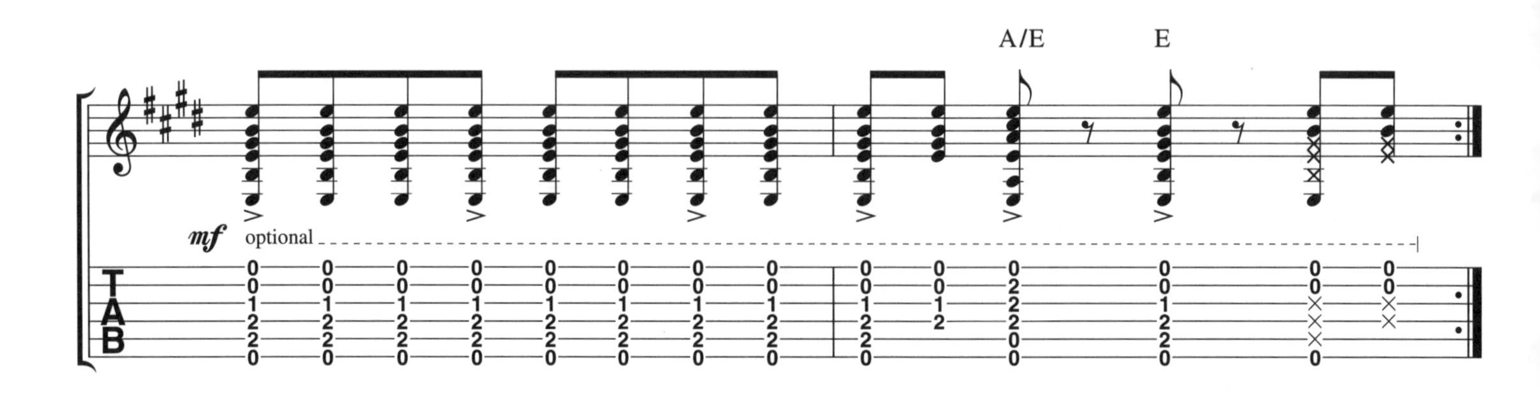
A/E
E
mf
optional
TAB

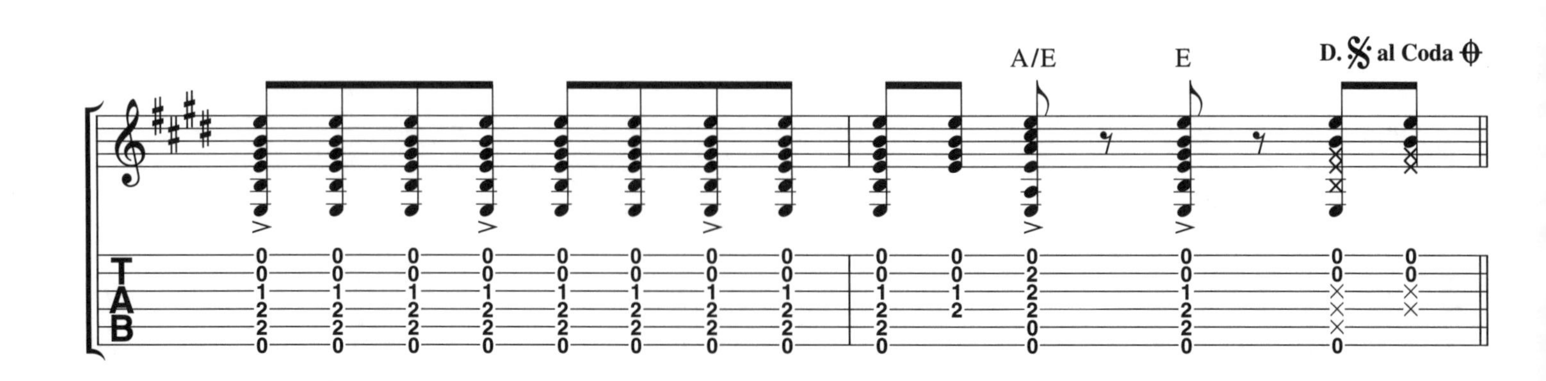
A/E
E
D.𝄋 al Coda ⊕
TAB

Coda

E A/E E A
Well love is love and not
E A E
fade a - way. L -
(E) A E A
love is love and not fade a - way.
E A E
Repeat to fade
Not fade a - way. Not

sunshine of your love

Words & Music by Jack Bruce, Pete Brown & Eric Clapton

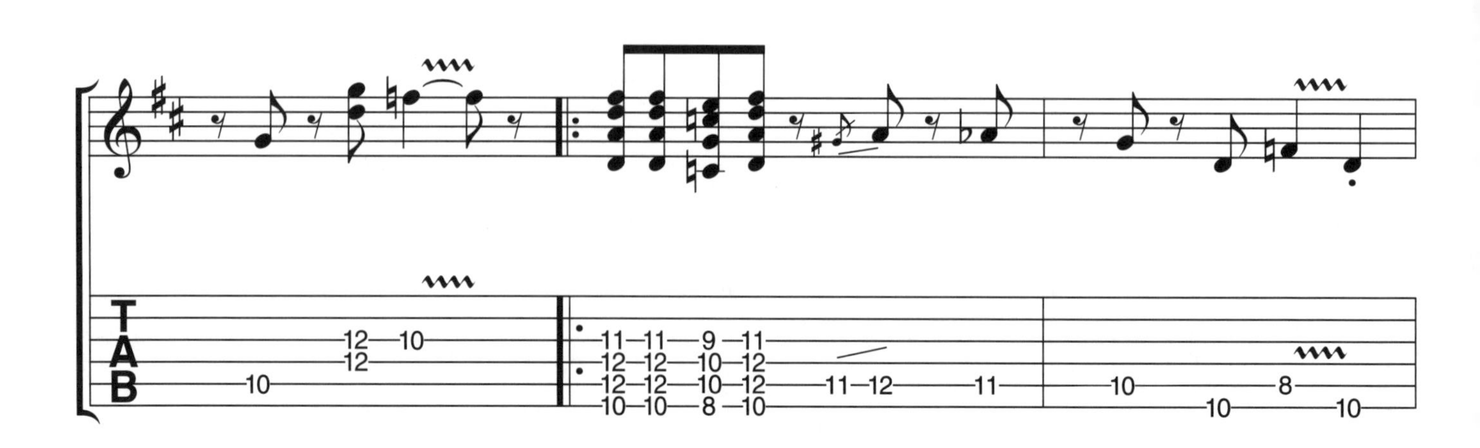

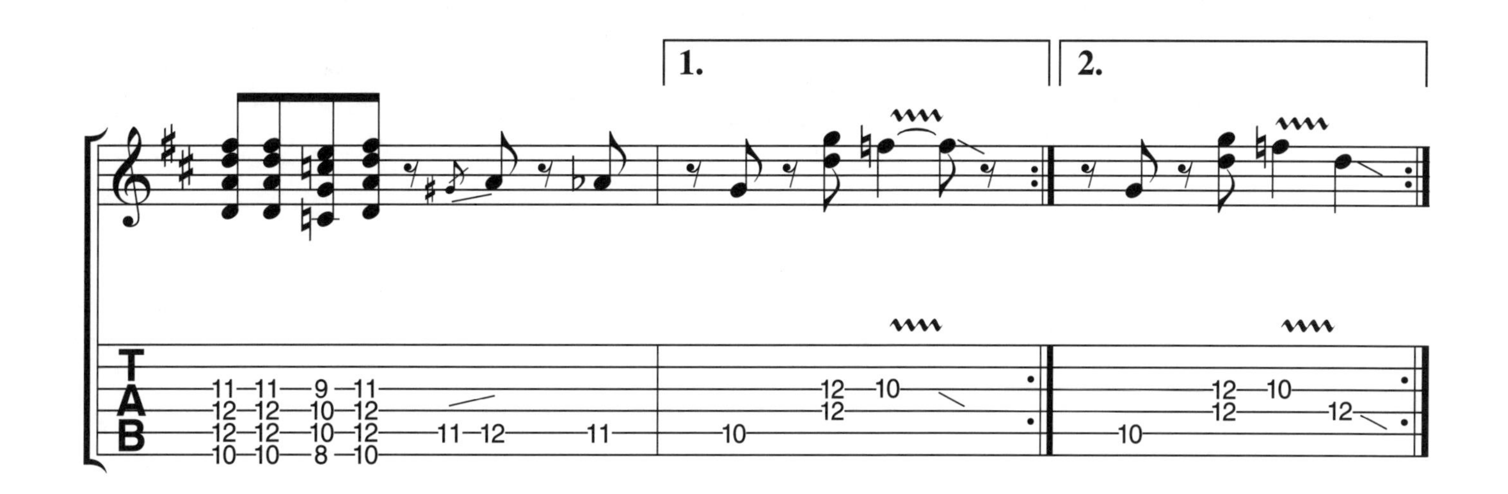
1.
2.
T
A
B

3.
A
1. Well it's get - ting near dawn, when
See Block Lyrics for Verses 2 & 3
T
A
B

lights close their tir - ed eyes, I'll soon be with you my love
2&3x
1x only
T
A
B
1x only

to give you my dawn sur - prise.
I'll
T
A
B

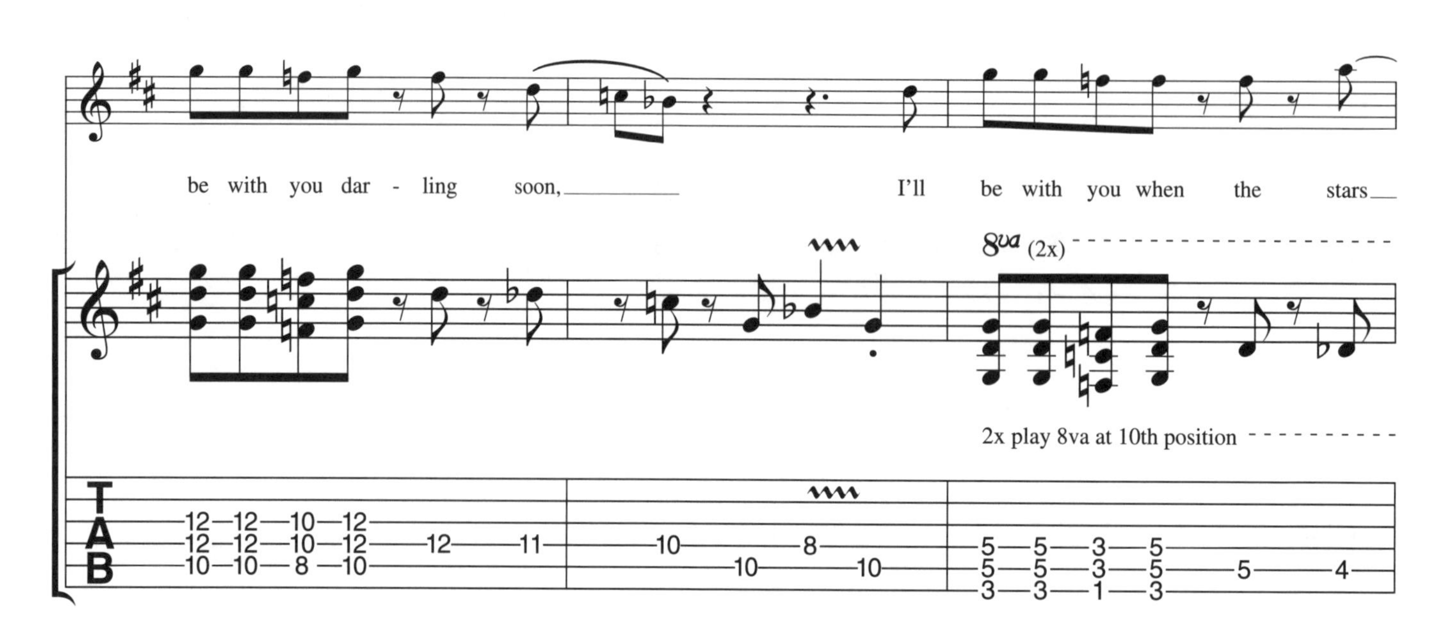
be with you dar - ling soon,
I'll be with you when the stars
8va (2x)
2x play 8va at 10th position
T
A
B

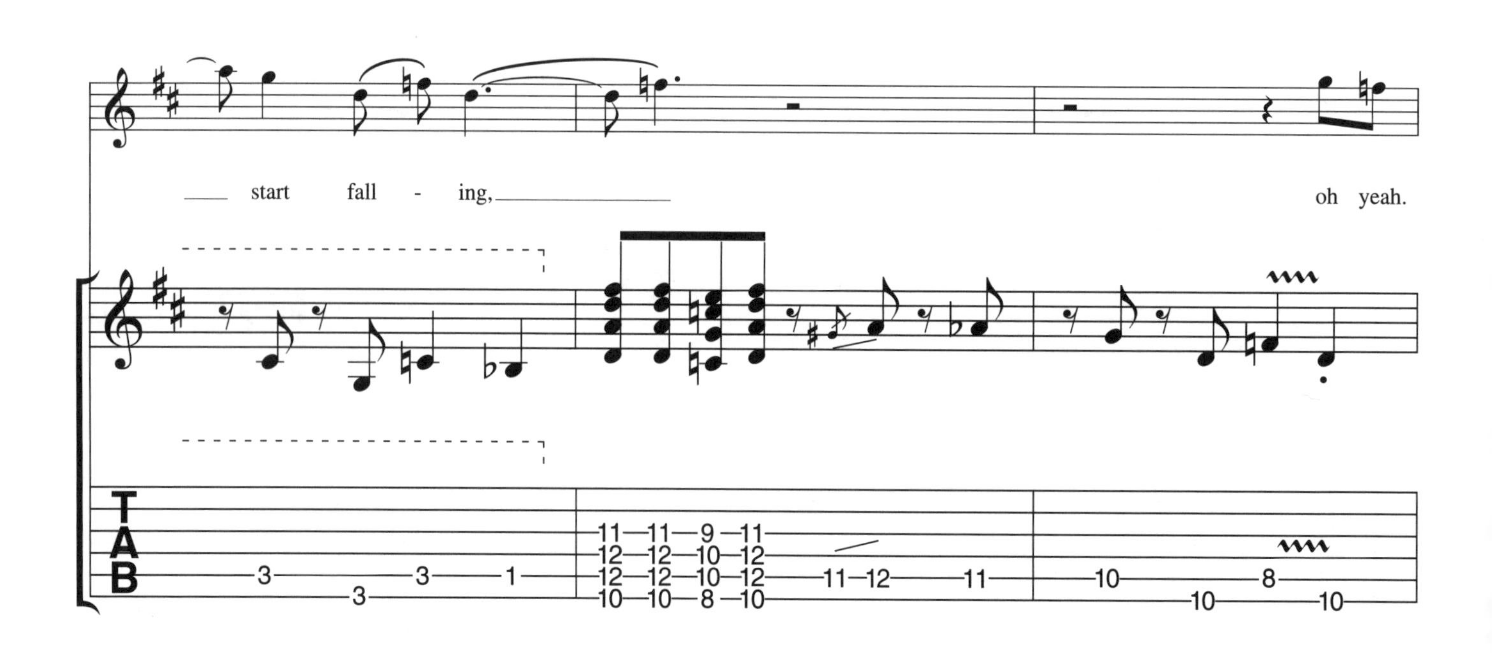
start fall - ing,
oh yeah.
T
A
B

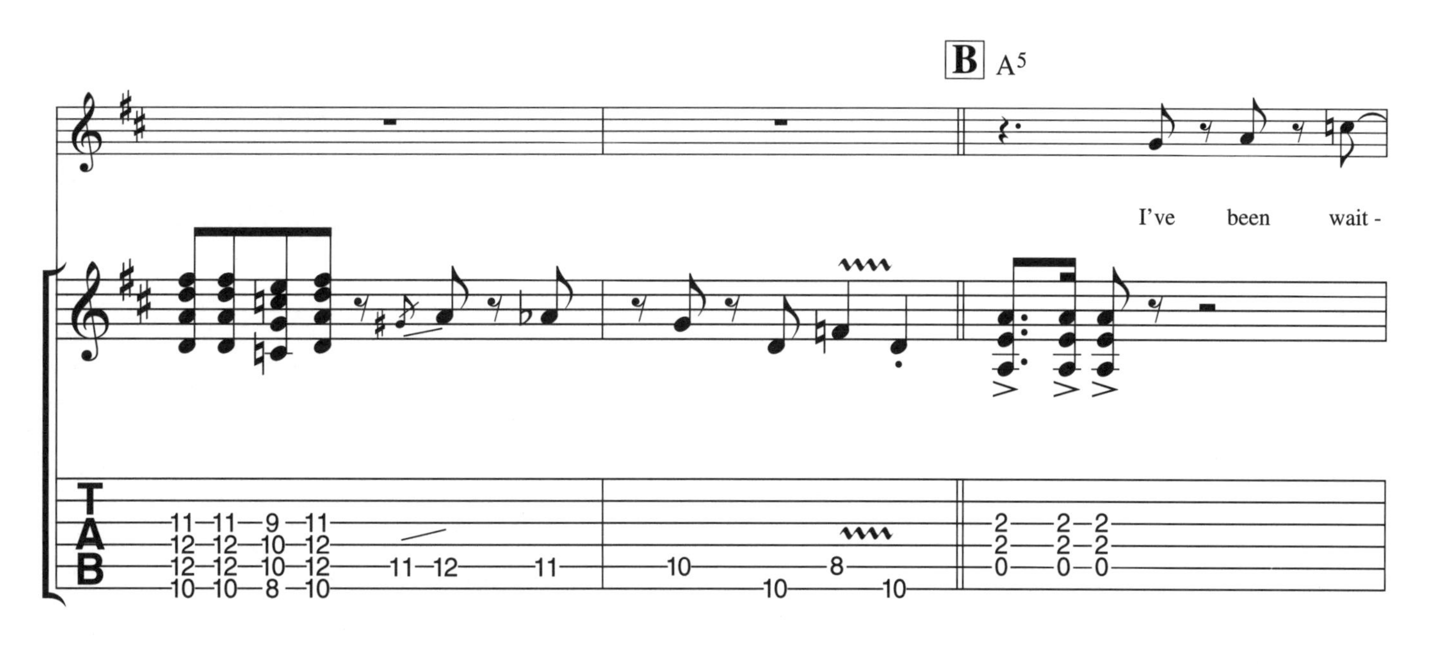
B
A5
I've been wait -

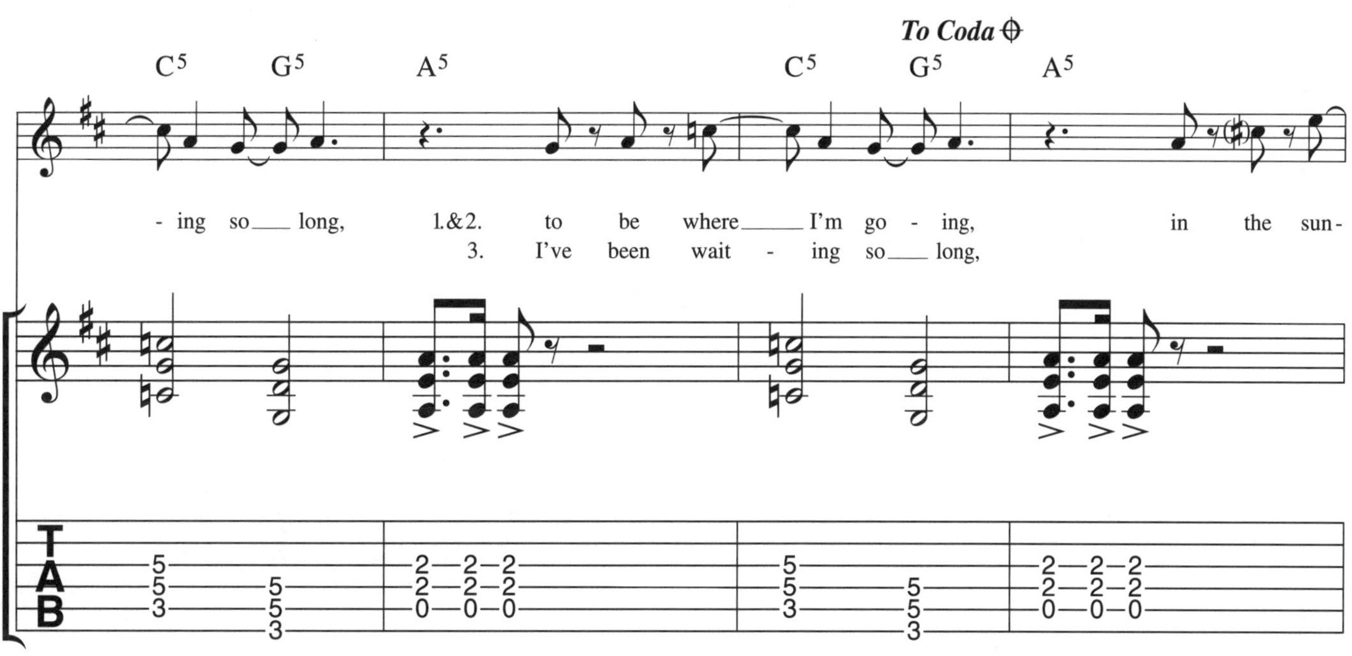
To Coda
C5
G5
A5
C5
G5
A5
- ing so long,
1.&2. to be where I'm go - ing,
3. I've been wait - ing so long,
in the sun-

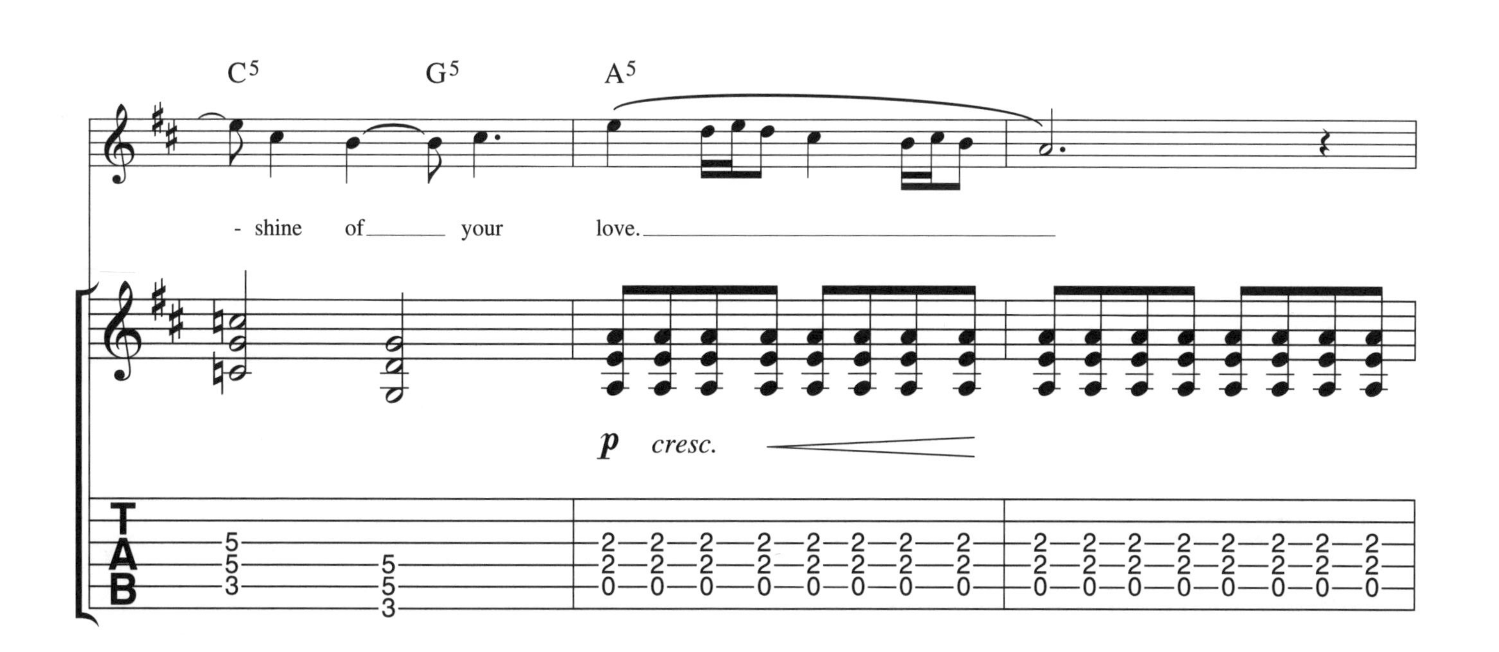
C5
G5
A5
- shine of your love.
p cresc.

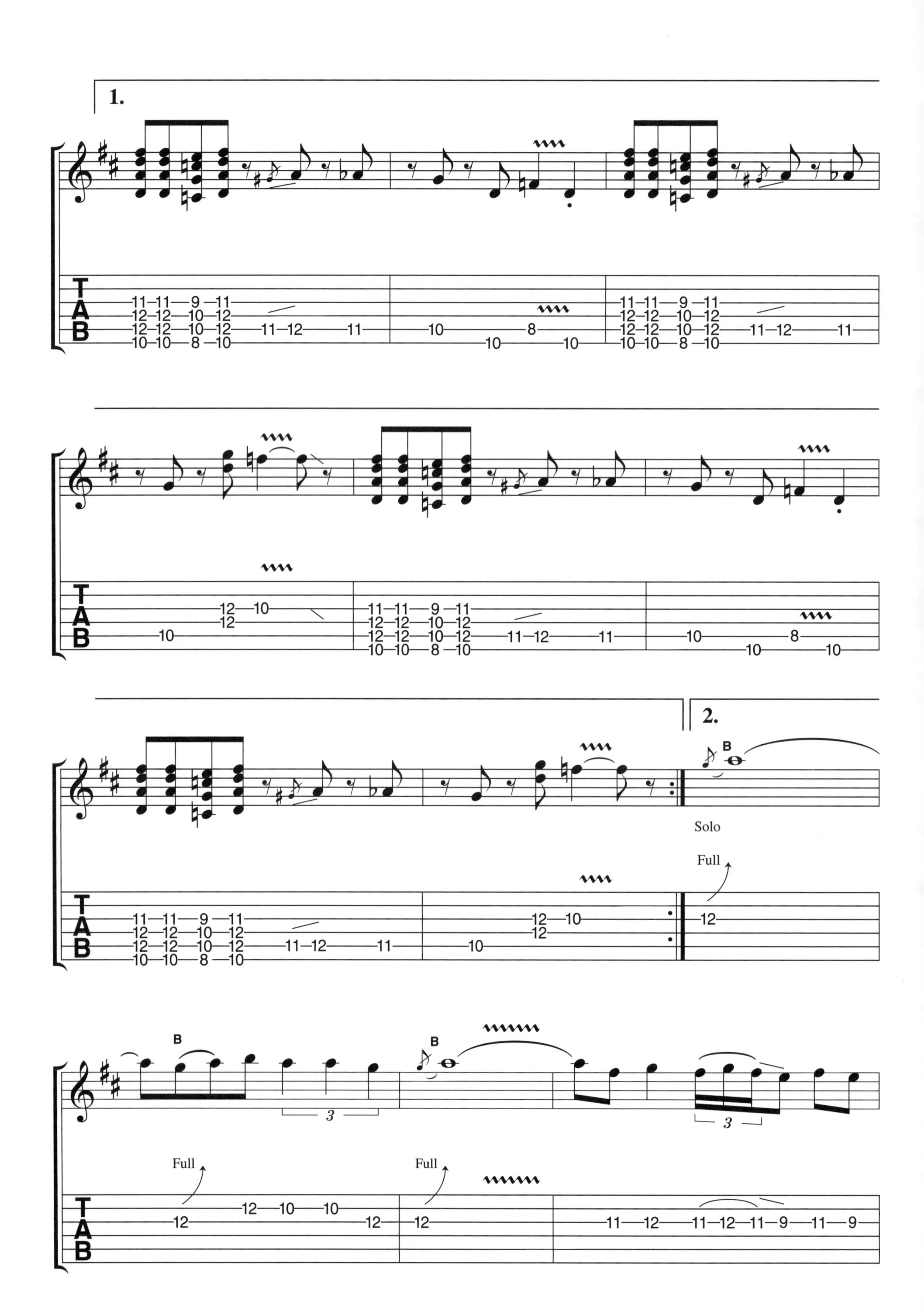

1.
2.
Solo
Full
B

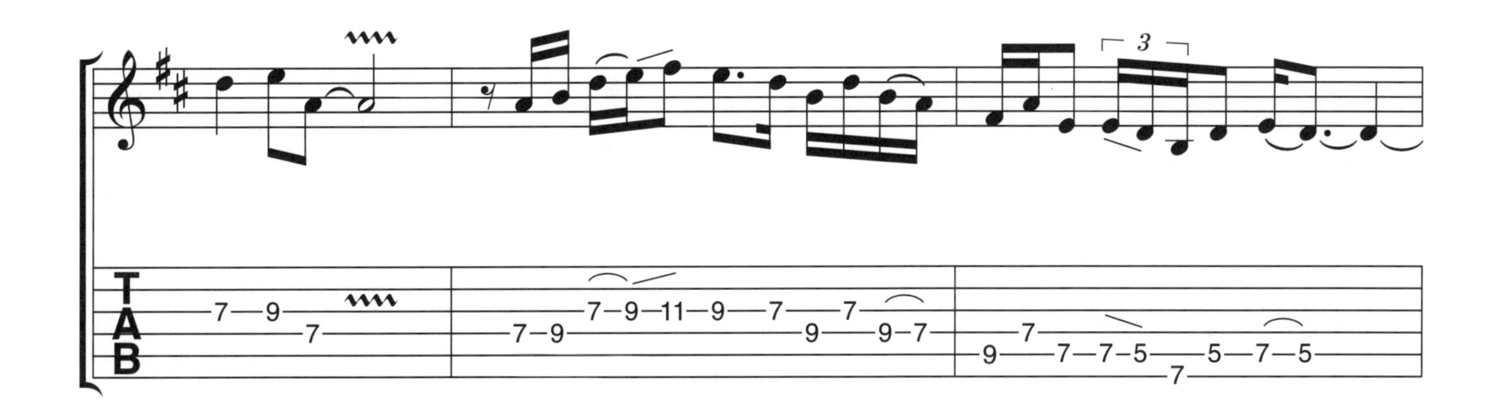
3
TAB
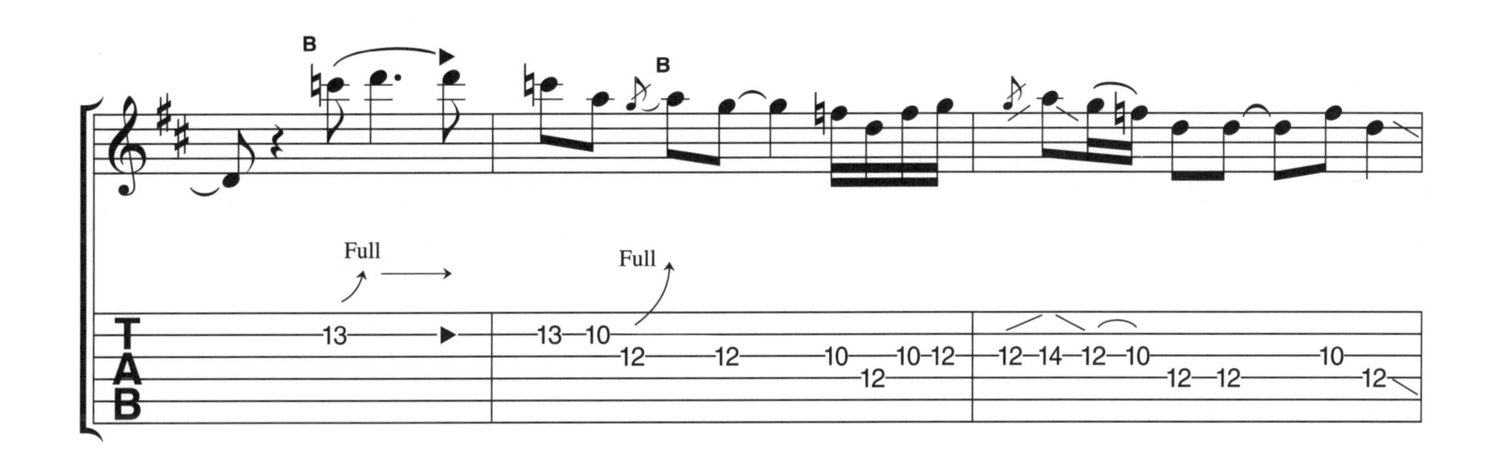
B
B
Full
Full
TAB
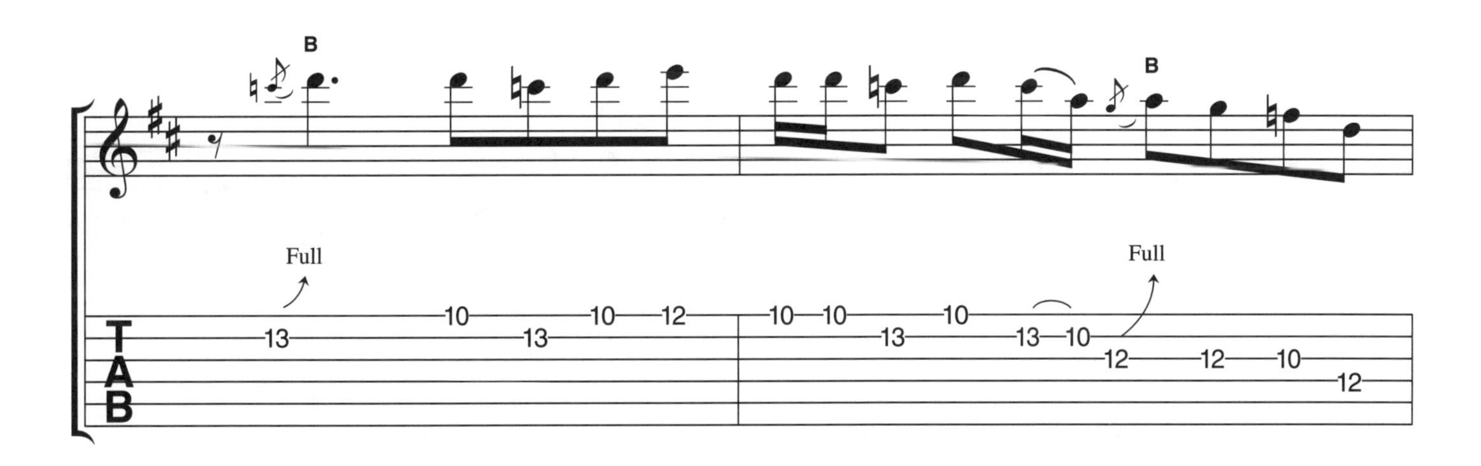
B
B
Full
Full
TAB
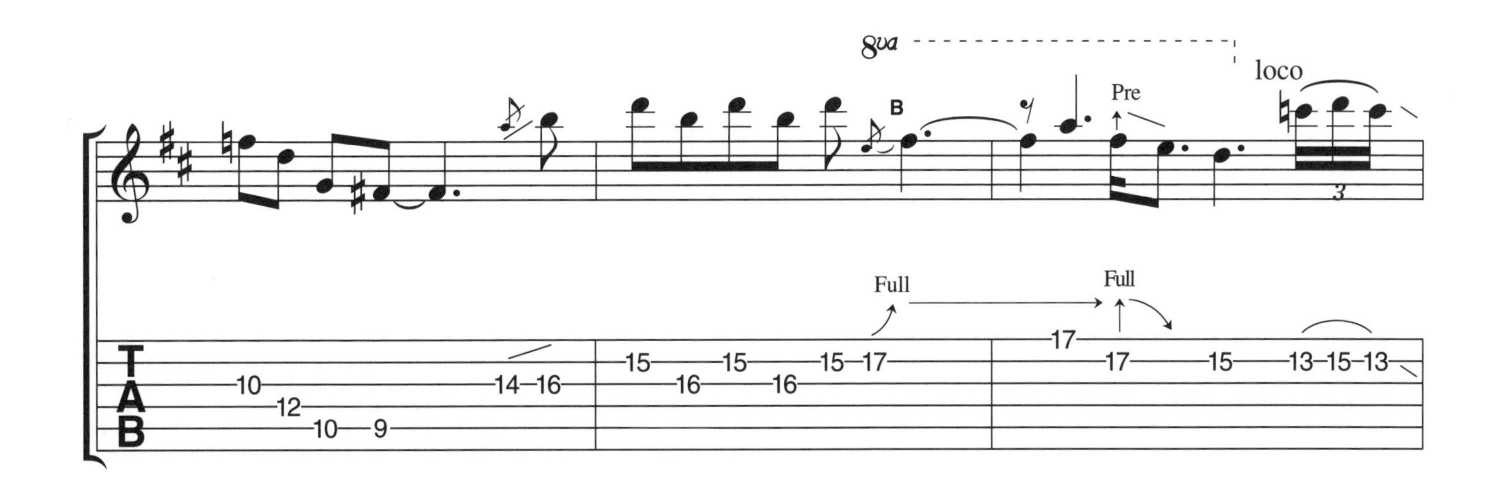
8va
loco
B
Pre
3
Full
Full
TAB

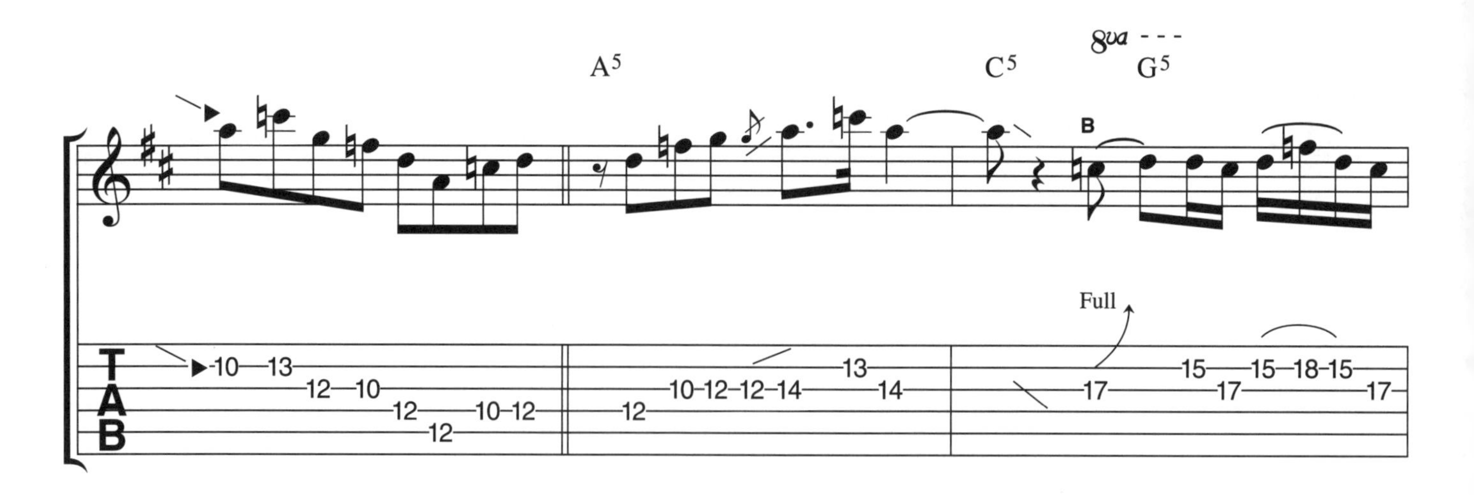
A5
C5
8va
G5
B
Full

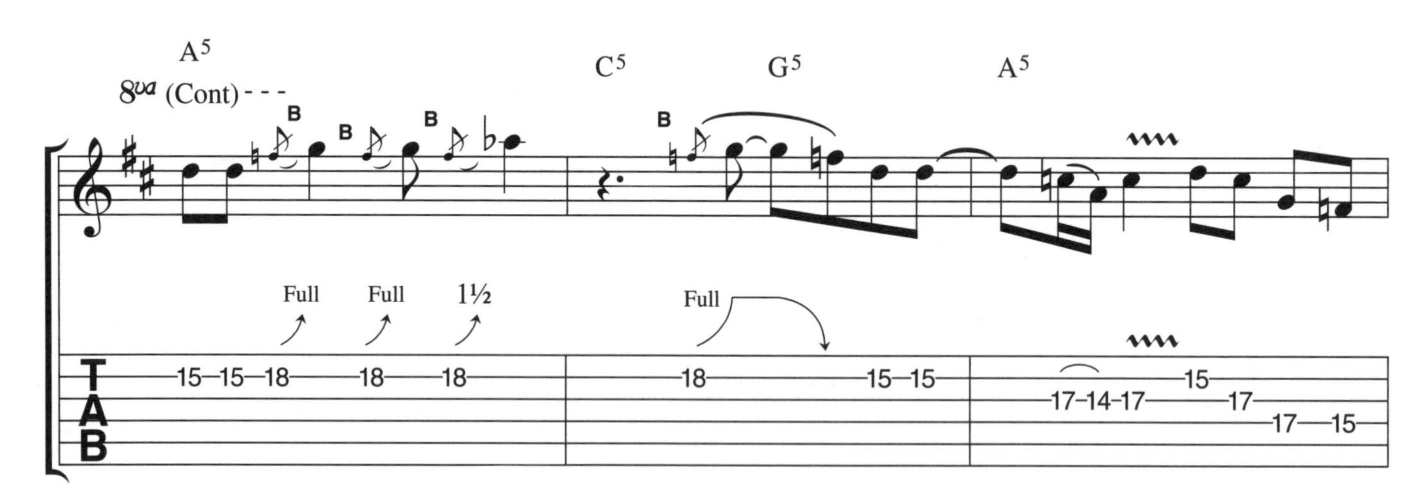
A5
8va (Cont)
B
Full
1½
C5
G5

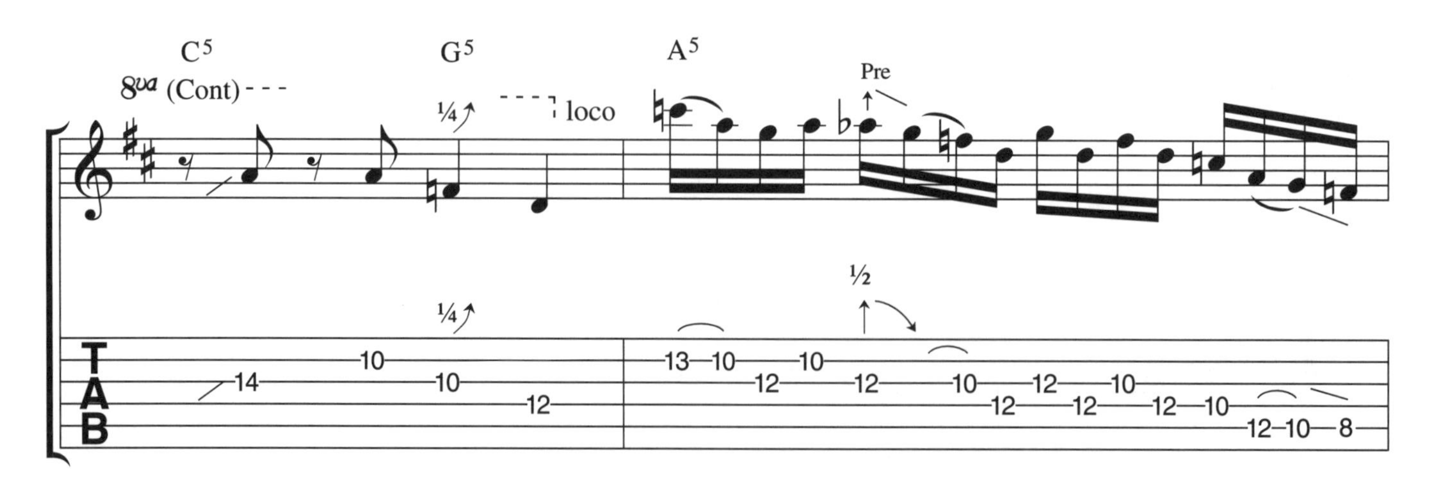
C5
8va (Cont)
G5
¼
loco
A5
Pre
½

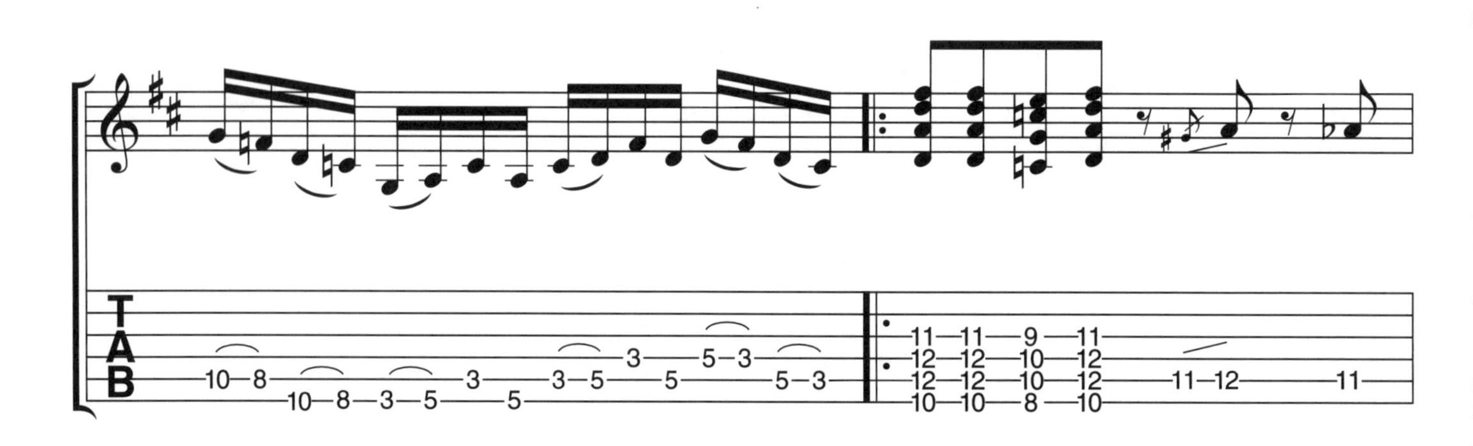

D.𝄋. al Coda ⊕

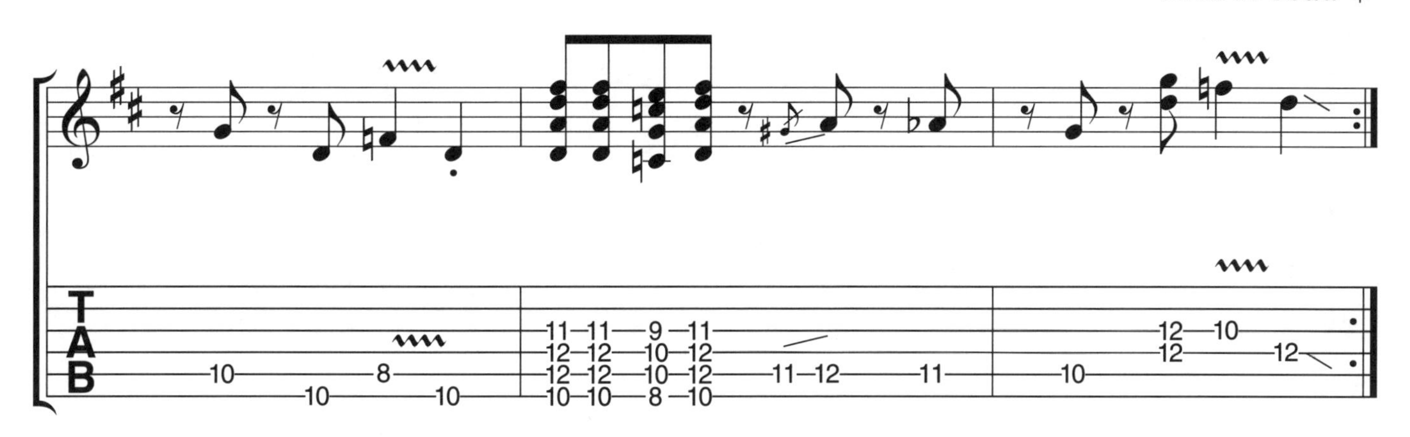

⊕ Coda
A5
C5
G5
A5
C5
G5
to be where I'm go - ing,
in the sun - shine of your

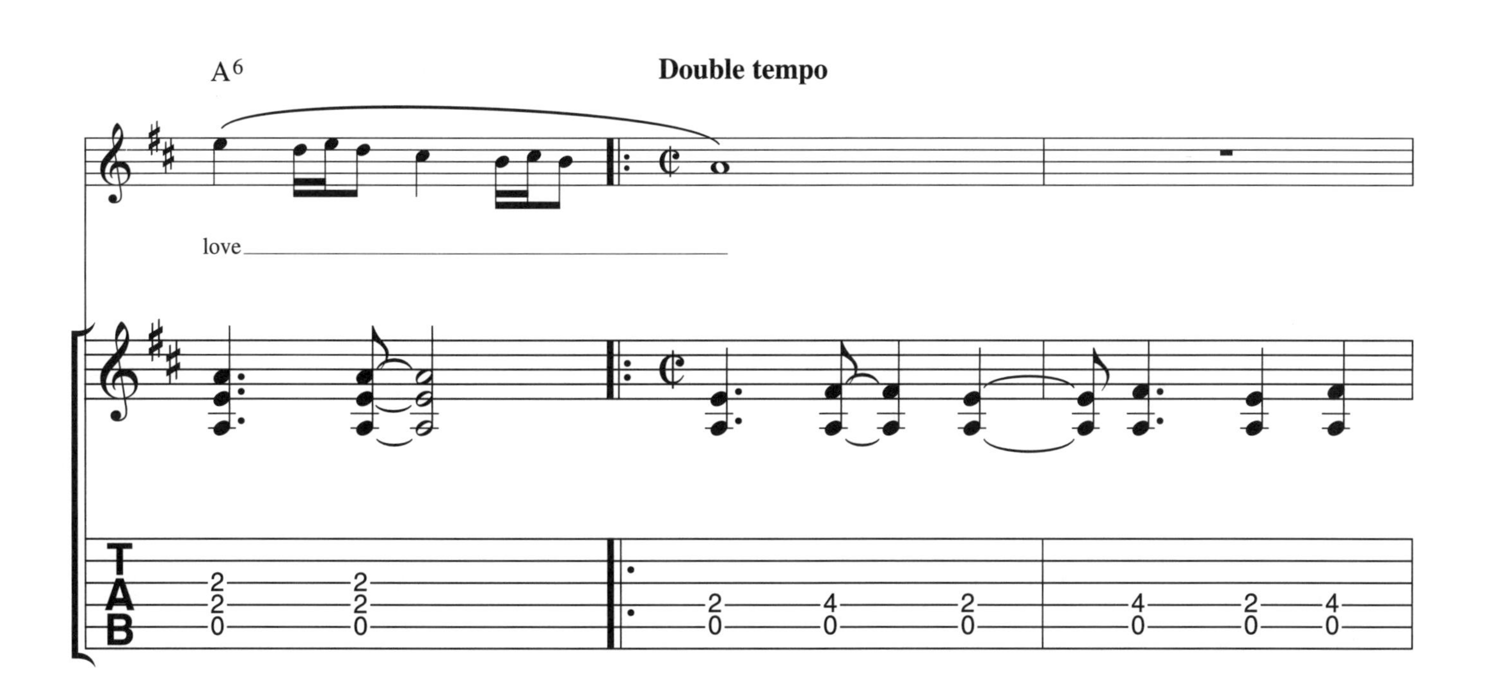
A6
Double tempo
love

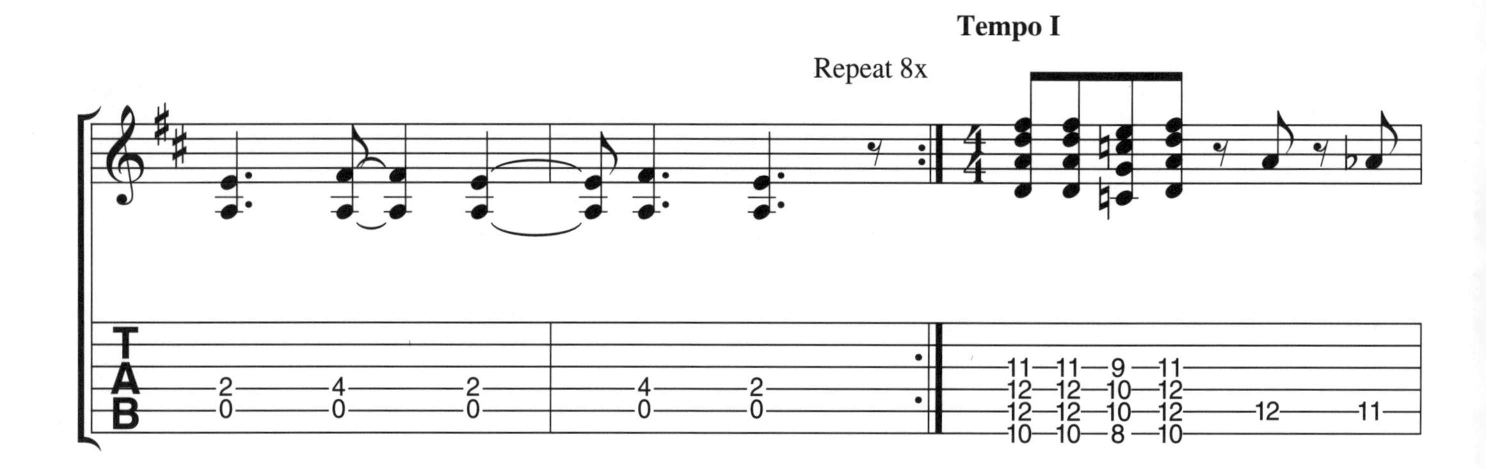

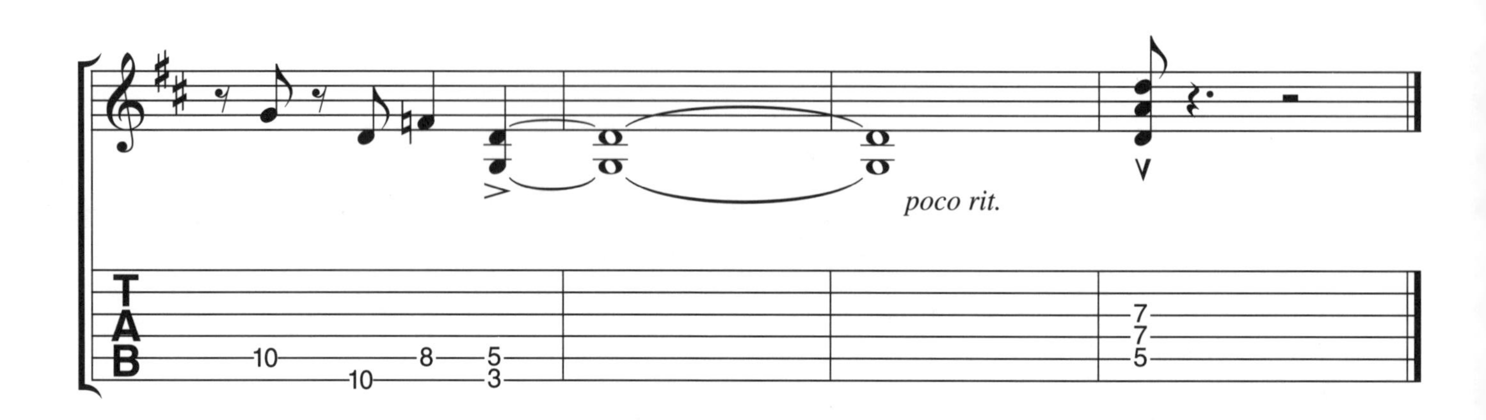

Verse 2:
I'm with you my love
The light's shining through on you
Yes, I'm with you my love.
It's the morning, and just we two.
I'll stay with you darling now
I'll stay with you till my seeds are dried up
(Oh yeah).

Verse 3:
It's getting near dawn
(When) lights close their tired eyes.
I'll soon be with you my love
(To) give you my dawn surprise.
I'll be with you darling soon
I'll be with you when the stars start falling
(Oh yeah).

Présentation De La Tablature De Guitare

Il existe trois façons différentes de noter la musique pour guitare : à l'aide d'une portée musicale, de tablatures ou de barres rythmiques.

Les BARRES RYTHMIQUES sont indiquées au-dessus de la portée. Jouez les accords dans le rythme indiqué. Les notes rondes indiquent des notes récilles.

La PORTÉE MUSICALE indique les notes et rythmes et est divisée en mesures. Cette division est représentée par des lignes. Les notes sont : do, ré, mi, fa, sol, la, si.

La PORTÉE EN TABLATURE est une représentation graphique des touches de guitare. Chaque ligne horizontale correspond à une corde et chaque chiffre correspond à une case.

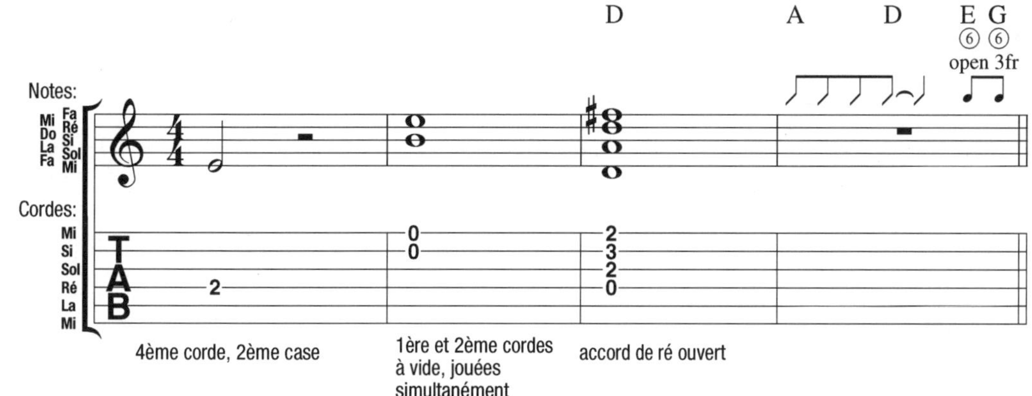

4ème corde, 2ème case

1ère et 2ème cordes à vide, jouées simultanément

accord de ré ouvert

Notation Spéciale De Guitare : Définitions

TIRÉ DEMI-TON : Jouez la note et tirez la corde afin d'élever la note d'un demi-ton (étape à moitié).

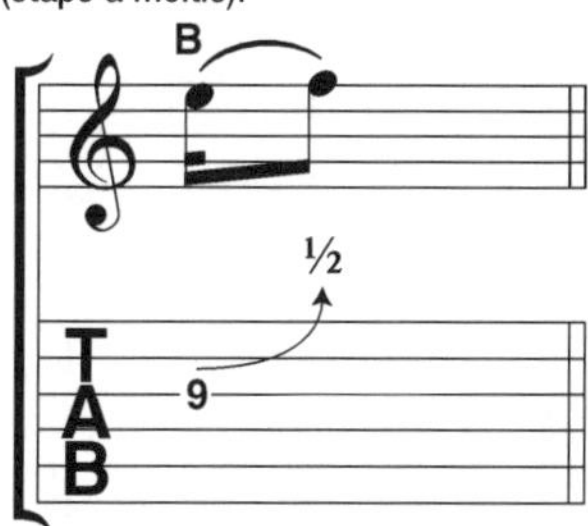

TIRÉ PLEIN : Jouez la note et tirez la corde afin d'élever la note d'un ton entier (étape entière).

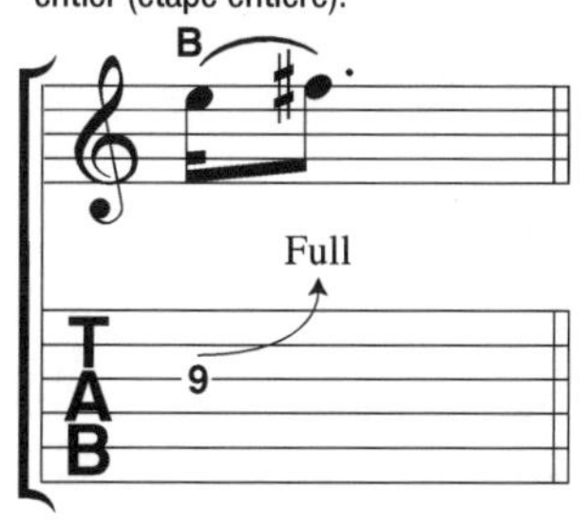

TIRÉ D'AGRÉMENT : Jouez la note et tirez la corde comme indiqué. Jouez la première note aussi vite que possible.

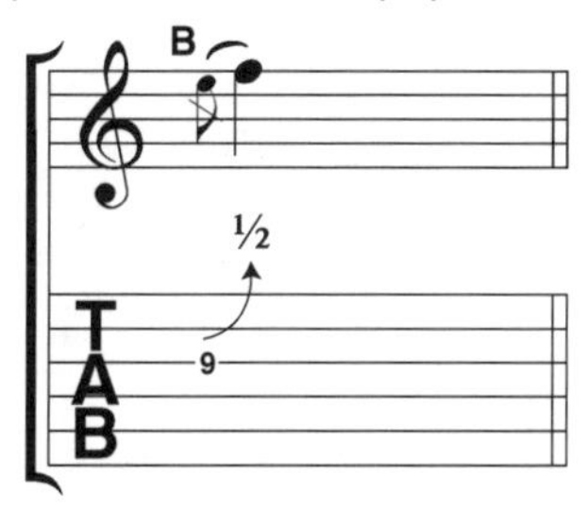

TIRÉ QUART DE TON : Jouez la note et tirez la corde afin d'élever la note d'un quart de ton.

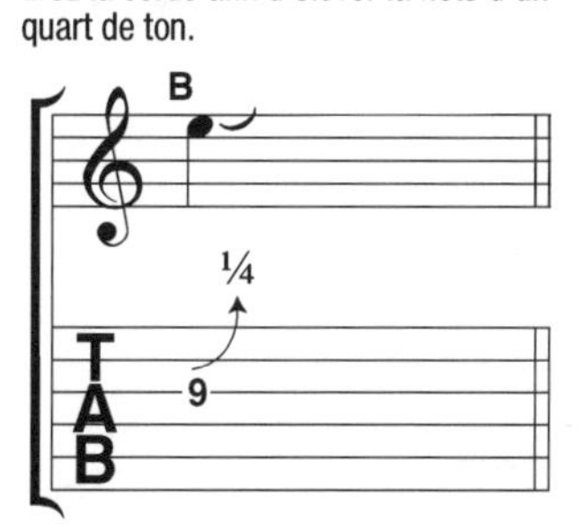

TIRÉ ET LÂCHÉ : Jouez la note et tirez la corde comme indiqué, puis relâchez, afin d'obtenir de nouveau la note de départ.

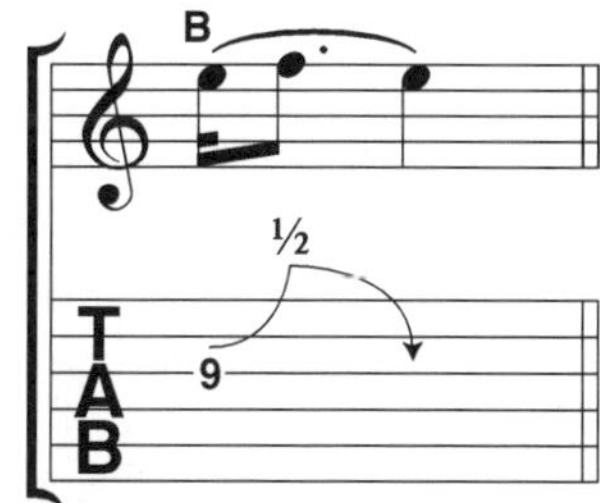

TIRÉ ET REJOUÉ : Jouez la note et tirez la corde comme indiqué puis rejouez la corde où le symbole apparaît.

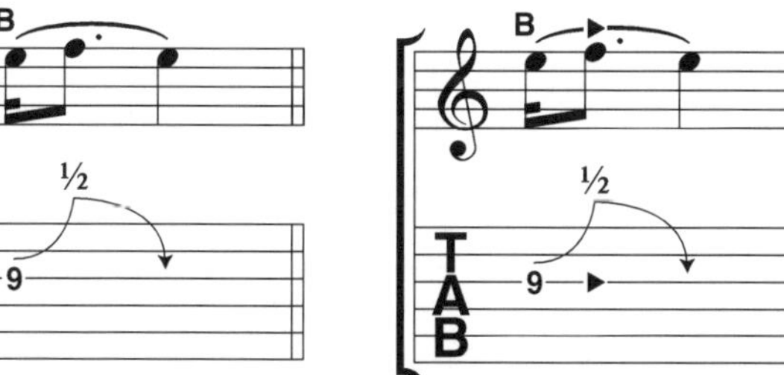

PRÉ-TIRÉ : Tirez la corde comme indiqué puis jouez cette note.

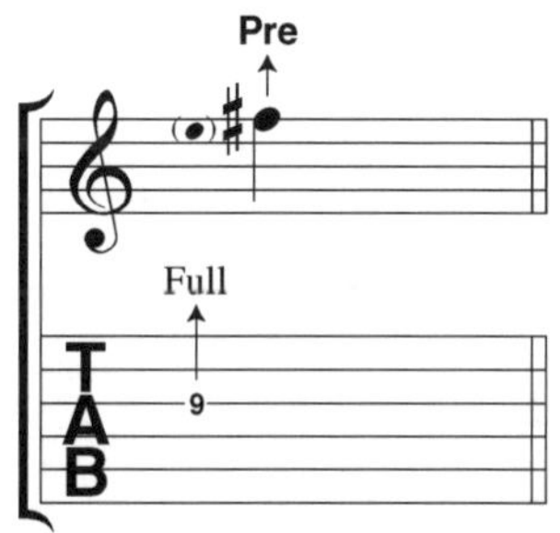

PRÉ-TIRÉ ET LÂCHÉ : Tirez la corde comme indiqué. Jouez la note puis relâchez la corde afin d'obtenir le ton de départ.

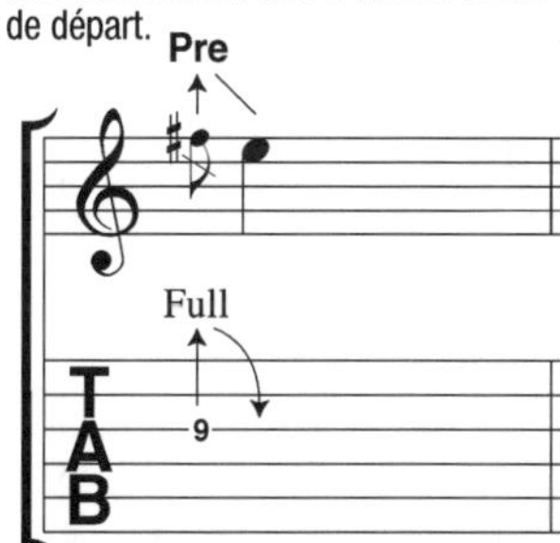

HAMMER-ON: Jouez la première note (plus basse) avec un doigt puis jouez la note plus haute sur la même corde avec un autre doigt, sur le manche mais sans vous servir du médiator.

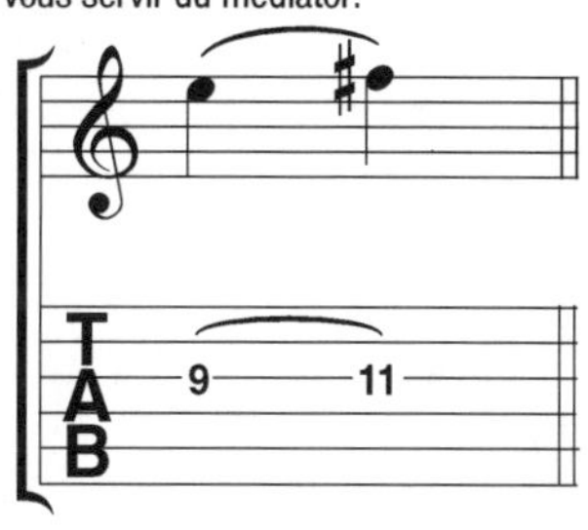

PULL-OFF: Positionnez deux doigts sur les notes à jouer. Jouez la première note et sans vous servir du médiator, dégagez un doigt pour obtenir la deuxième note, plus basse.

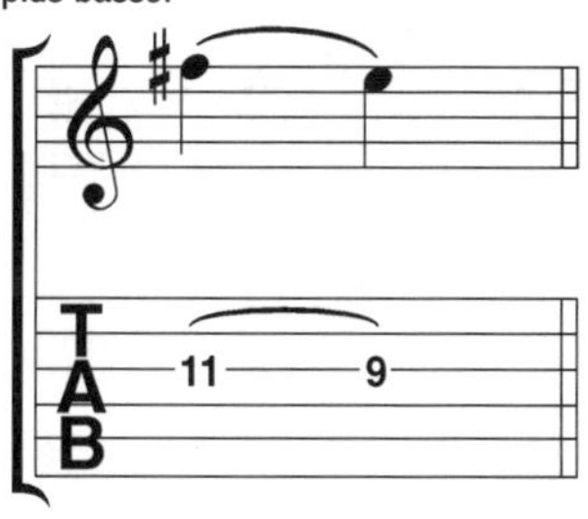

GLISSANDO : Jouez la première note puis faites glisser le doigt le long du manche pour obtenir la seconde note qui, elle, n'est pas jouée.

GLISSANDO ET REJOUÉ : Identique au glissando à ceci près que la seconde note est jouée.

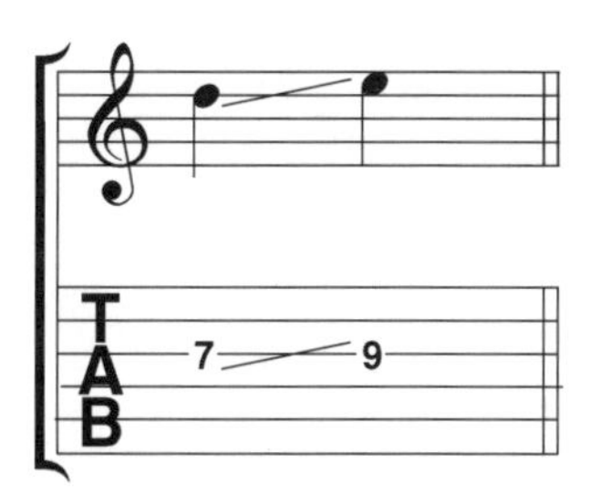

HARMONIQUES NATURELLES : Jouez la note tandis qu'un doigt effleure la corde sur le manche correspondant à la case indiquée.

PICK SCRAPE (SCRATCH) : On fait glisser le médiator le long de la corde, ce qui produit un son éraillé.

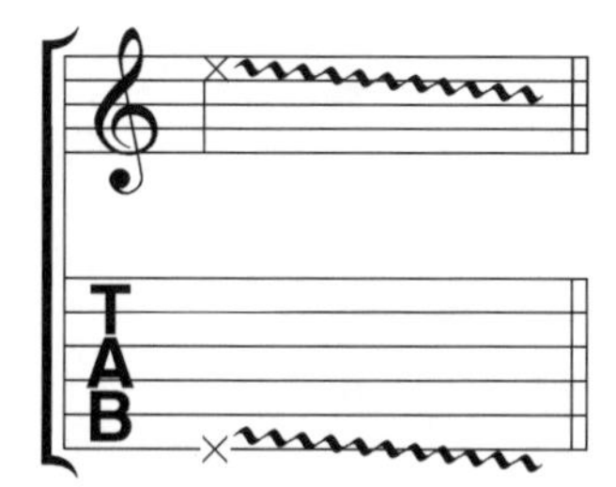

ÉTOUFFÉ DE LA PAUME : La note est partiellement étouffée par la main (celle qui se sert du médiator). Elle effleure la (les) corde(s) juste au-dessus du chevalet.

P.M.

0 0 0 0

CORDES ÉTOUFFÉES : Un effet de percussion produit en posant à plat la main sur le manche sans relâcher, puis en jouant les cordes avec le médiator.

NOTE: La vitesse des tirés est indiquée par la notation musicale et le tempo.

Erläuterung zur Tabulaturschreibweise

Es gibt drei Möglichkeiten, Gitarrenmusik zu notieren: im klassichen Notensystem, in Tabulaturform oder als rhythmische Akzente.

RHYTHMISCHE AKZENTE werden über dem Notensystem notiert. Geschlagene Akkorde werden rhythmisch dargestellt. Ausgeschriebene Noten stellen Einzeltöne dar.

Im **NOTENSYSTEM** werden Tonhöhe und rhythmischer Verlauf festgelegt; es ist durch Taktstriche in Takte unterteilt. Die Töne werden nach den ersten acht Buchstaben des Alphabets benannt.
Beachte: "B" in der anglo-amerkanischen Schreibweise entspricht dem deutschen "H"!

DIE TABULATUR ist die optische Darstellung des Gitarrengriffbrettes. Jeder horizontalen Linie ist eine bestimmte Saite zugeordnet, jede Zahl bezeichnet einen Bund.

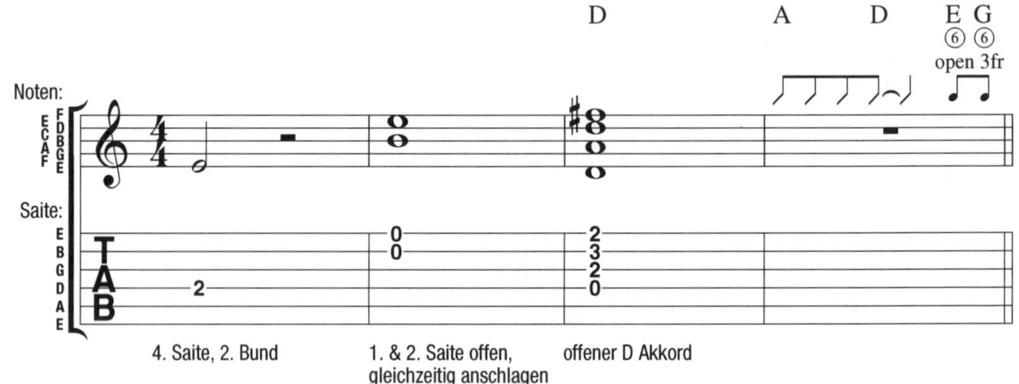

Erklärungen zur speziellen Gitarennotation

HALBTON-ZIEHER: Spiele die Note und ziehe dann um einen Halbton höher (Halbtonschritt).

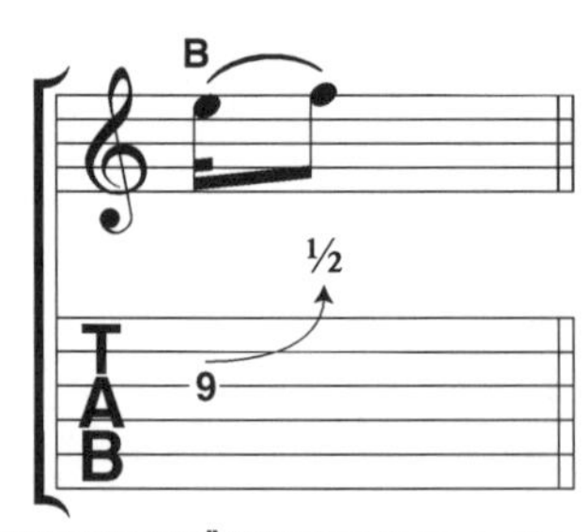

GANZTON-ZIEHER: Spiele die Note und ziehe dann einen Ganzton höher (Ganztonschritt).

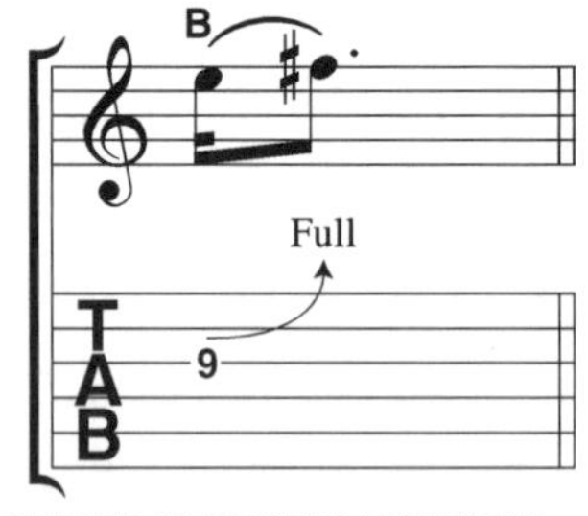

ZIEHER MIT VORSCHLAG: Spiele die Note und ziehe wie notiert. Spiele die erste Note so schnell wie möglich.

VIERTELTON-ZIEHER: Spiele die Note und ziehe dann einen Viertelton höher (Vierteltonschritt).

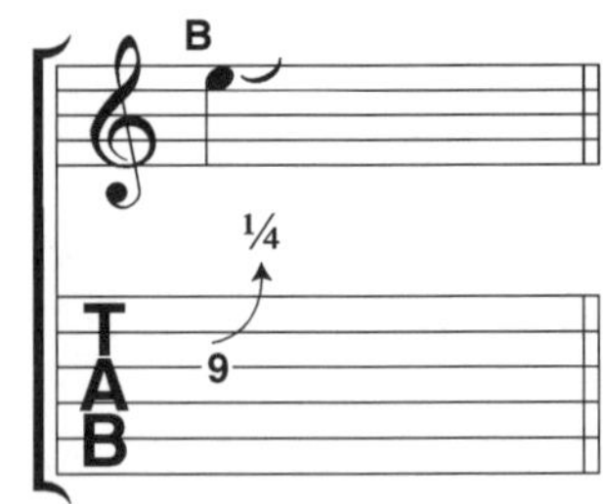

ZIEHEN UND ZURÜCKGLEITEN: Spiele die Note und ziehe wie notiert; lasse den Finger dann in die Ausgangposition zurückgleiten. Dabei wird nur die erste Note angeschlagen.

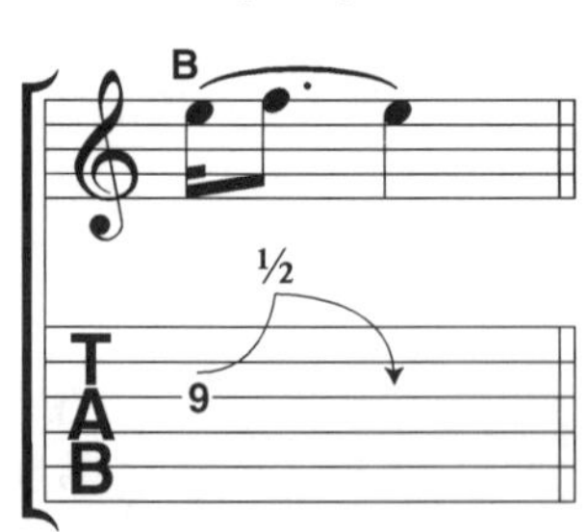

ZIEHEN UND NOCHMALIGES ANSCHLAGEN: Spiele die Note und ziehe wie notiert, schlage die Saite neu an, wenn das Symbol "▶" erscheint und lasse den Finger dann zurückgleiten.

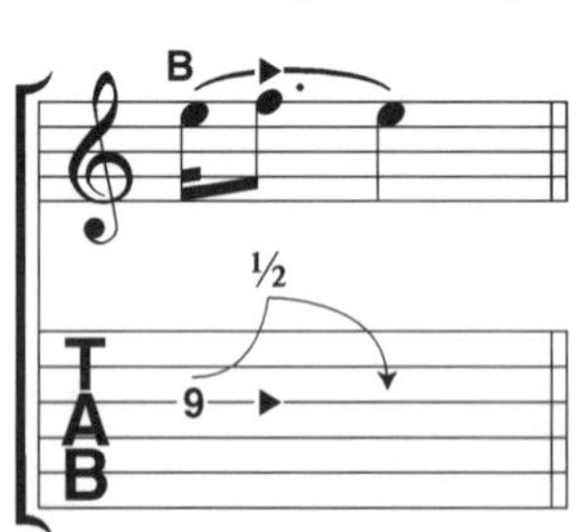

ZIEHER VOR DEM ANSCHLAGEN: Ziehe zuerst die Note wie notiert; schlage die Note dann an.

ZIEHER VOR DEM ANSCHLAGEN MIT ZURÜCKGLEITEN: Ziehe die Note wie notiert; schlage die Note dann an und lasse den Finger auf die Ausgangslage zurückgleiten.

AUFSCHLAGTECHNIK: Schlage die erste (tiefere) Note an; die höhere Note (auf der selben Saite) erklingt durch kräftiges Aufschlagen mit einem anderen Finger der Griffhand.

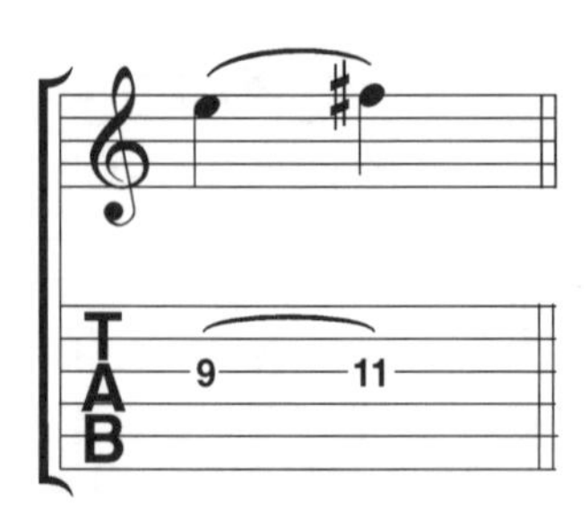

ABZIEHTECHNIK: Setze beide Finger auf die zu spielenden Noten und schlage die erste Note an. Ziehe dann (ohne nochmals anzuschlagen) den oberen Finger der Griffhand seitlich - abwärts ab, um die zweite (tiefere) Note zum klingen zu bringen.

GLISSANDOTECHNIK: Schlage die erste Note an und rutsche dann mit dem selben Finger der Griffhand aufwärts oder abwärts zur zweiten Note. Die zweite Note wird nicht angeschlagen.

GLISSANDOTECHNIK MIT NACHFOLGENDEM ANSCHLAG: Gleiche Technik wie das gebundene Glissando, jedoch wird die zweite Note angeschlagen.

NATÜRLICHES FLAGEOLETT: Berühre die Saite über dem angegebenen Bund leicht mit einem Finger der Griffhand. Schlage die Saite an und lasse sie frei schwingen.

PICK SCRAPE: Fahre mit dem Plektrum nach unten über die Saiten - klappt am besten bei umsponnenen Saiten.

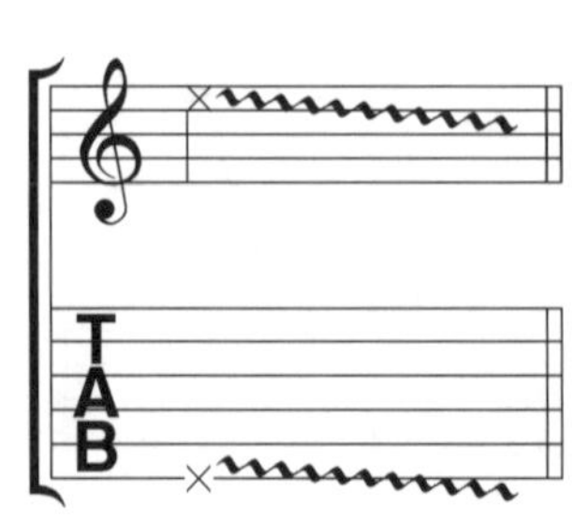

DÄMPFEN MIT DER SCHLAGHAND: Lege die Schlaghand oberhalb der Brücke leicht auf die Saite(n).

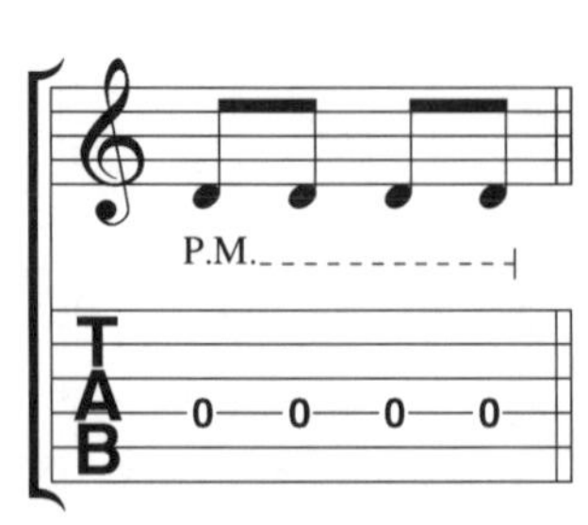

DÄMPFEN MIT DER GRIFFHAND: Du erreichst einen percussiven Sound, indem du die Griffhand leicht über die Saiten legst (ohne diese herunterzudrücken) und dann mit der Schlaghand anschlägst.

AMMERKUNG: Das Tempo der Zieher und Glissandos ist abhängig von der rhythmischen Notation und dem Grundtempo.

Spiegazioni Di Tablatura Per Chitarra

La musica per chitarra può essere annotata in tre diversi modi: sul pentagramma, in tablatura e in taglio ritmico

IL TAGLIO RITMICO è scritto sopra il pentagramma. Percuotere le corde al ritmo indicato Le teste arrotondate delle note indicano note singole.

IL PENTAGRAMMA MUSICALE mostra toni e ritmo ed è divisa da linee in settori. I toni sono indicati con le prime sette lettere dell'alfabeto.

LA TABLATURA rappresenta graficamente la tastiera della chitarra. Ogni linea orizzontale rappresenta una corda, ed ogni corda rappresenta un tasto.

4° corda, 2° tasto

1° e 2° corda aperte, suonate insieme

accordo D aperto

Definizioni Per Annotazioni Speciali Per Chitarra

SEMI-TONO CURVATO: percuotere la nota e curvare di un semitono (1/2 passo).

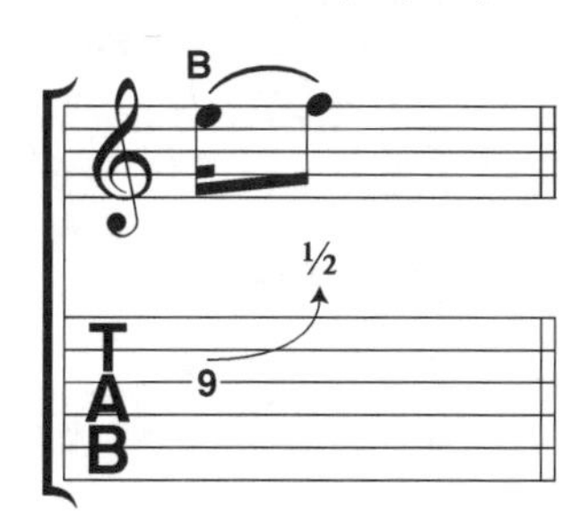

TONO CURVATO: Percuotere la nota e curvare di un tono (passo intero).

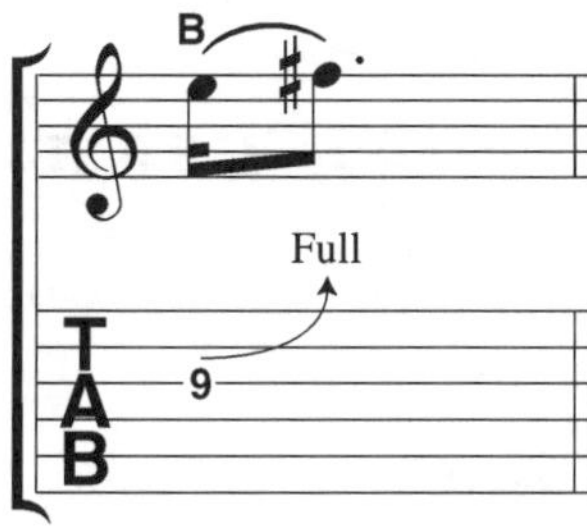

NOTA BREVE, CURVATA: percuotere la nota e curvare come indicato. Suonare la prima nota il più velocemente possibile.

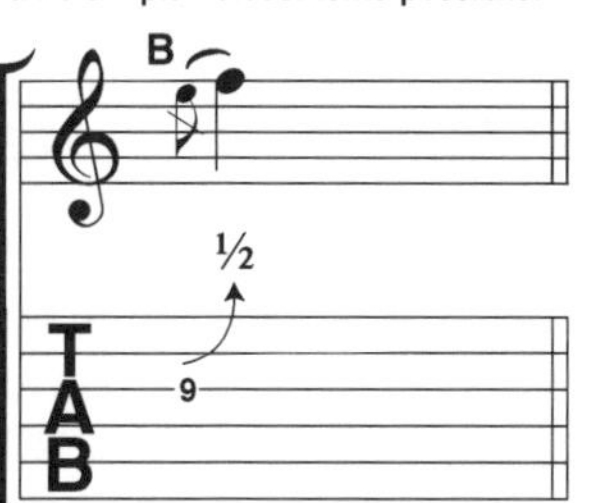
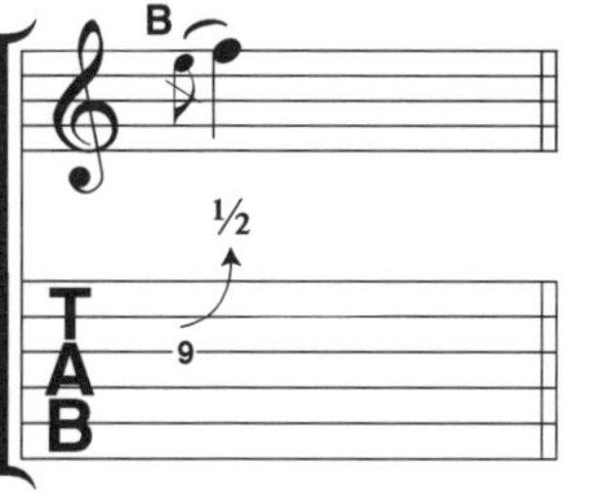

QUARTO DI TONO, CURVATO: Percuotere la nota e curvare di un quarto di passo.

CURVA E LASCIA: Percuotere la nota e curvare come indicato, quindi rilasciare indietro alla nota originale.

CURVA E RIPERCUOTI: Percuotere la nota e curvare come indicato poi ripercuotere la corda nel punto del simbolo.

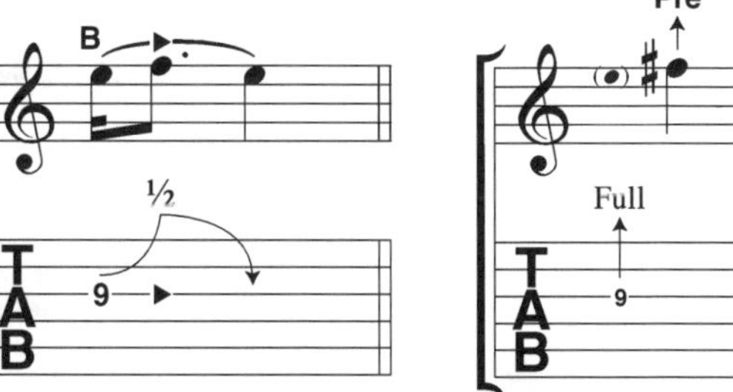
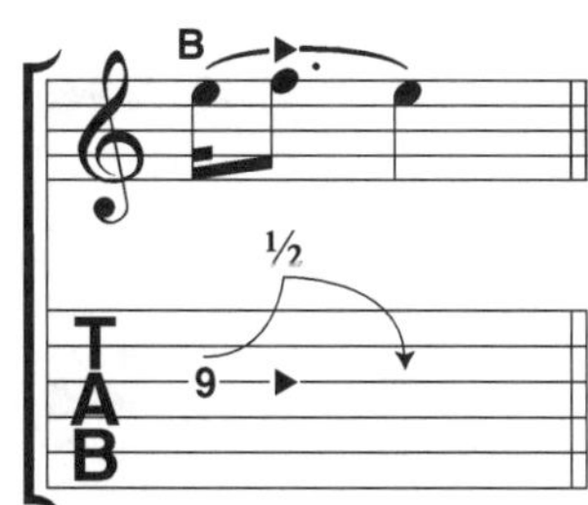

PRE-CURVA: Curvare la nota come indicato e quindi percuoterla.

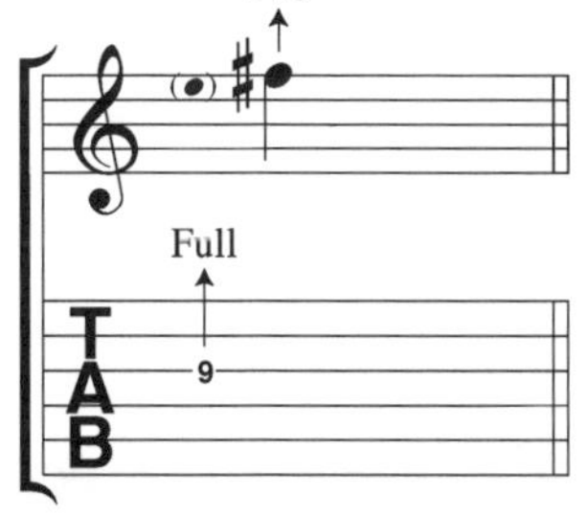

PRE-CURVA E RILASCIO: Curvare la nota come indicato. Colpire e rilasciare la nota indietro alla tonalità indicata.

MARTELLO-COLPISCI: Colpire la prima nota (in basso) con un dito; quindi suona la nota più alta (sulla stessa corda) con un altro dito, toccandola senza pizzicare.

TOGLIERE: Posizionare entrambe le dita sulla nota da suonare. Colpire la prima nota e, senza pizzicare, togliere le dita per suonare la seconda nota (più in basso).

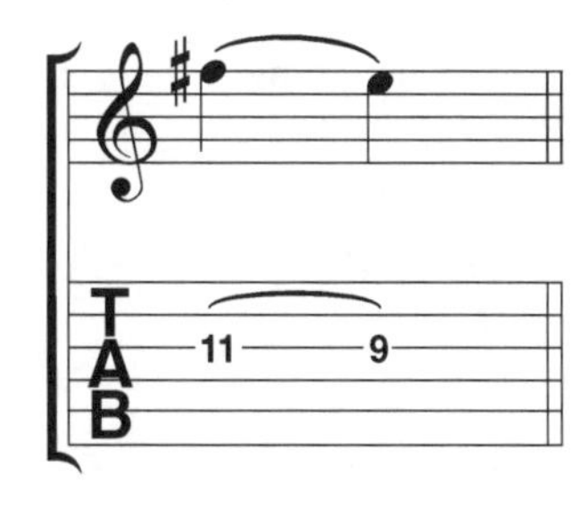

LEGATO SCIVOLATO (GLISSATO): Colpire la prima nota e quindi far scivolare lo stesso dito della mano della tastiera su o giù alla seconda nota. La seconda nota non viene colpita.

CAMBIO SCIVOLATO (GLISSARE E RICOLPIRE): Uguale al legato - scivolato eccetto che viene colpita la seconda nota.

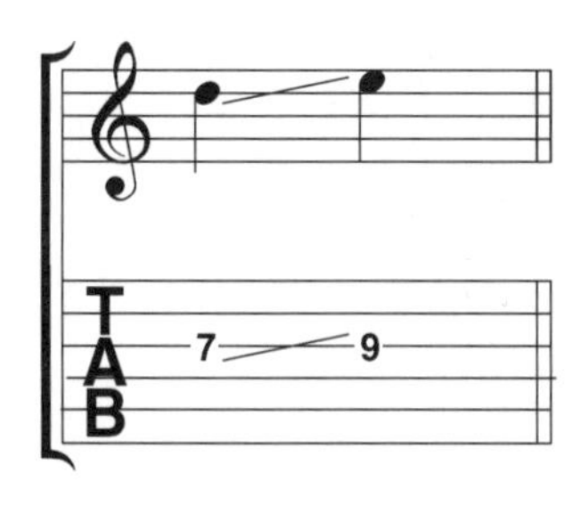

ARMONICA NATURALE: Colpire la nota mentre la mano della tastiera tocca leggermente la corda direttamente sopra il tasto indicato.

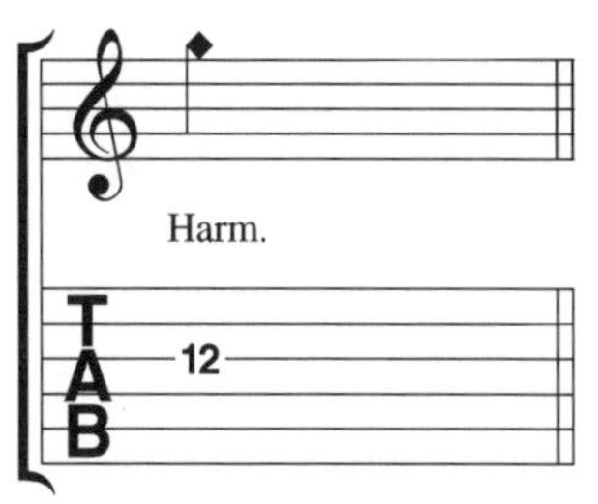

PIZZICA E GRAFFIA: Il limite del pizzicato è tirato su (o giù) lungo la corda, producendo un suono graffiante.

SORDINA CON IL PALMO: La nota è parzialmente attenuato dalla mano del pizzicato toccando la corda (le corde) appena prima del ponte.

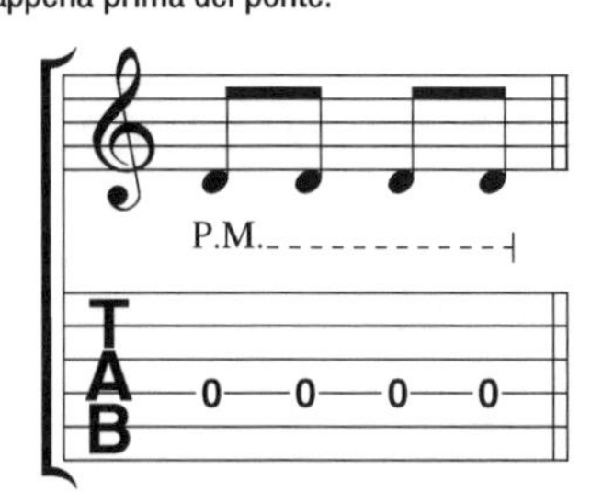

CORDE SMORZATE: Un suono di percussione viene prodotto appoggiando la mano della tastiera attraverso la corda (le corde) senza premere, e colpendole con la mano del pizzicato.

NOTA: La velocità di ogni curvatura è indicata dalle annotazioni musicali e dal tempo.

Collect *all* the titles in the series!

play guitar with...

AC/DC
Includes:
back in black
highway to hell
whole lotta rosie
Order No. AM955900

the beatles
Includes:
day tripper
get back
yesterday
Order No. NO90665

the beatles Book 2
Includes:
eight days a week
please please me
ticket to ride
Order No. NO90667

the beatles Book 3
Includes:
here comes the sun
revolution
while my guitar gently weeps
Order No. NO90689

chuck berry
Includes:
around and around
johnny b. goode
no particular place to go
Order No. AM943789

black sabbath
Includes:
iron man
paranoid
war pigs
Order No. AM955911

blur
Includes:
country house
girls and boys
parklife
Order No. AM935320

bon jovi
Includes:
livin' on a prayer
wanted dead or alive
you give love a bad name
Order No. AM92558

eric clapton
Includes:
layla
sunshine of your love
tears in heaven
Order No. AM950862

phil collins
Includes:
another day in paradise
don't lose my number
one more night
Order No. AM928147

the cranberries
Includes:
hollywood
ridiculous thoughts
zombie
Order No. AM941699

dire straits
Includes:
money for nothing
romeo and juliet
sultans of swing
Order No. DG70735

david gilmour
Includes:
learning to fly
on the turning away
take it back
Order No.AM954602

buddy holly
Includes:
rave on
words of love
peggy sue
Order No. AM943734

john lee hooker
Includes:
boom boom
the healer
i'm in the mood
Order No. AM951885

b.b. king
Includes:
every day i have the blues
rock me baby
the thrill is gone
Order No. AM951874

the kinks
Includes:
all day and all of the night
waterloo sunset
you really got me
Order No. AM951863

kula shaker
Includes:
govinda
hey dude
hush
Order No. AM943767

john lennon
Includes:
cold turkey
happy xmas (war is over)
woman
Order No. AM943756

bob marley
Includes:
i shot the sheriff
jamming
no woman, no cry
Order No. AM937739

metallica
Includes:
enter sandman
fade to black
the unforgiven
Order No. AM92559

metallica Book 2
Includes:
creeping death
seek and destroy
whiskey in the jar
Order No. AM955977

alanis morissette
Includes:
hand in my pocket
ironic
you oughta know
Order No. AM943723

oasis
Includes:
cigarettes & alcohol
morning glory
supersonic
Order No. AM935330

ocean colour scene
Includes:
the circle
the day we caught the train
the riverboat song
Order No. AM943712

elvis presley
Includes:
all shook up
blue suede shoes
hound dog
Order No. AM937090

pulp
Includes:
common people
disco 2000
sorted for e's & wizz
Order No. AM938124

the rolling stones
Includes:
brown sugar
(i can't get no) satisfaction
jumpin' jack flash
Order No. AM90247

sting
Includes:
an englishman in new york
fields of gold
if you love somebody
set them free
Order No. AM928092

the stone roses
Includes:
i am the resurrection
i wanna be adored
ten storey love song
Order No. AM943701

the stone roses Book 2
Includes:
fool's gold
love spreads
one love
Order No. AM955890

paul weller
Includes:
the changingman
out of the sinking
wild wood
Order No. AM937827

the who
Includes:
i can see for miles
pinball wizard
substitute
Order No. AM955867

the gold book
Includes:
johnny b. goode (chuck berr
layla (eric clapton)
sultans of swing (dire straits
Order No. AM951907

the platinum boo
Includes:
a design for life (manic stree
preachers)
cigarettes & alcohol (oasis)
the riverboat song
(ocean colour scene)
Order No. AM951918

the 60's
Includes:
all along the watchtower
(jimi hendrix)
born to be wild (steppenwol
not fade away (the rolling st
Order No. AM957748

the 70's
Includes:
all right now (free)
hotel california (the eagles)
live and let die (wings)
Order No. AM957759

the 80's
Includes:
addicted to love (robert pal
need you tonight (inxs)
where the streets have no
name (u2)
Order No. AM957760

the 90's
Includes:
everything must go
(manic street preachers)
love is the law (the seahorse
wonderwall (oasis)
Order No. AM957770